FEMA 100
A Century of Great Taste

ISBN 10: 0615270298
ISBN 13: 978-0-615-27029-6

Acknowledgements

FEMA would like to express its sincere appreciation and gratitude

to everyone who provided the information and insight that helped

make this book possible. We would especially like to thank

Tim Adams, Cathy Cook, Mike Davis, Dolf De Rovira, Hamed Faridi,

Richard Hall, John Hallagan, Nancy Higley, Pat Hoffman,

Ben Katzenstein, Charles Manley, Cynthia Mussinan,

Richard Pisano Sr., Glenn Roberts, Skip Rosskam,

Howard Smith Jr., Fred Stults, John Walradt, and Tim Webster.

We are particularly grateful to Mary Treisbach,

who came on board at a critical time and played

a key role in making this publication a reality.

PREFACE

As co-chair of the FEMA 100th anniversary committee, I join Howard Smith Jr. in thanking the many individuals who helped bring this major project to the finish line. So many industry volunteers and amateur historians offered their insights and memories to make this history of FEMA come alive for all of us.

I hope that as you read this book, you will develop a clear understanding of the important role FEMA has played in the development of our industry. Our goal is to share FEMA's rich history with members and potential members alike. If you are a current member, I hope you will learn something new while experiencing the pride and satisfaction I do when I read about FEMA's many great accomplishments.

If you are a prospective member, I urge you to join us and become a part of FEMA's next hundred years. With FEMA membership, you will have access to many resources that will more than pay for themselves each year. Our strategic focus on science, advocacy, volunteers and leadership, education and training, communication, global relations and emerging issues ensures that FEMA will continue to provide the utmost value to all of our members.

You will also have an opportunity as an individual to work with FEMA on committee assignments that will expand your knowledge and share your expertise in a way that is well-founded in the FEMA tradition.

FEMA is an extraordinary organization.

FEMA has flourished for a century because we have been fortunate in having dedicated participation and a spirit of collegiality and respect among our member companies. By helping one another, we help our industry and the consumers we serve, and reap the benefits of mutual cooperation.

A note for readers who are outside of our industry: We are glad to have the opportunity to share just a taste of what FEMA has been and continues to be. Our industry is unique — and our efforts through FEMA to sustain it responsibly are just part of our legacy.

Finally, on a personal note, McCormick & Company has been an ardent and active supporter of FEMA since the association's inception in 1909. I was honored to be the sixth FEMA president from McCormick, following in the footsteps of our founder and first FEMA president, Willoughby McCormick, his grandnephew, C.P. McCormick Jr., and Dr. Richard Hall, whose mark on the industry during the past 50 years has been significant and indelible.

Enjoy our history — and be proud of a century of good taste.

Hamed Faridi

Co-Chair, FEMA 100th

Anniversary Committee

Past-President, FEMA

Vice President, R&D

McCormick & Company

FEMA Member List – 2009

A.M. Todd Company	Citrus and Allied Essences Ltd.
Adron, Incorporated	Comax Flavors Corporation
Advanced Biotech	ConAgra Foods
Agilex Flavors & Fragrances, Inc.	Consumers Flavoring Extract Company, Inc.
Ajinomoto AminoScience, LLC.	Cott Beverages USA Inc.
Allured Business Media	CSA Imports
Altria Client Services Inc.	Custom Blending, Inc.
Apple Flavors & Fragrances USA Corp.	D.D. Williamson & Co., Inc.
Ariel Research/3E Company	Dammann & Company, Incorporated
Arylessence, Inc.	David Michael & Co., Inc.
Astral Extracts, Ltd.	Domino Specialty Ingredients
Aust & Hachmann (Canada) Ltd.	E & J Gallo Winery
Bacardi-Martini Product Development, Inc.	Edlong Dairy Flavors
Bedoukian Research, Inc.	Elan Chemical Company
Bell Flavors & Fragrances, Inc.	Firmenich, Inc.
Berjé, Incorporated	Flavor & Fragrance Specialties
Blue Pacific Flavors and Fragrances Inc.	Flavor Dynamics, Inc.
BNP Media	Flavor Infusion, LLC
Bongrain North America	Fleurchem Incorporated
Brand Aromatics, Inc.	Flexitral, Inc.
Cadbury plc	FONA International Inc.
California Custom Fruits and Flavors	Food Product Design/Virgo Publishing
Cargill Flavor Systems	Frutarom USA Inc.
Centerchem, Inc.	Givaudan
Charabot & Company, Inc.	H.B. Taylor Co.
Chart Corporation dba Naturex	Industrial Software, Inc.
Chemia Corporation	INNOVA, A Griffith Laboratories Company
Citromax Flavors	Institute of Food Technologists

International Flavors & Fragrances Inc.	Sethness Products Company
Kerry Ingredients & Flavours	Shasta Beverages, Inc.
Kraft Foods	Silesia Flavors Inc.
Lorillard Tobacco Company	Soda Aromatic Co., Ltd.
MANE Inc.	South Georgia Pecan Company, Inc.
McCormick & Company	Star Kay White, Inc.
Medallion International, Inc.	Stepan Company
Millennium Specialty Chemicals, Inc.	Symrise, Inc.
Mission Flavors & Fragrances, Inc.	Synergy Flavors, Inc.
National Fruit Flavor Company, Inc.	T. Hasegawa USA
Nielsen-Massey Vanillas, Incorporated	Takasago International Corporation (USA)
Northwestern Flavors, LLC	Tate and Lyle
Ottens Flavors	The Coca-Cola Company
Penta International Corporation	The Foote & Jenks Corporation
PepsiCo	The Hershey Company
Perfetti Van Melle	The Procter & Gamble Company
Pernod Ricard USA	TIC Gums Incorporated
Philip Morris International	Treatt USA
Phoenix Aromas & Essential Oils, Inc.	Tripper, Inc.
Polarome International	Ungerer & Company Incorporated
PROVA, Inc.	Vanilla Corporation of America, LLC
R. J. Reynolds Tobacco Company	Virginia Dare Extract Co., Inc.
Redpoint Bio Corporation	W & g Flavors Incorporated
Robertet, Inc.	Wen International Inc.
San-Ei Gen F.F.I. (USA), Inc.	Whittle & Mutch, Inc.
Select Products	Wild Flavors, Inc.
Senomyx, Inc.	Wynn Starr Flavors, Inc.
Sensient Flavors	

Presidents

1909-1912: W. M. McCormick, McCormick & Company

1912-1914: S.J. Sherer, Sherer-Gillette Company

1914-1915: S.H. Baer, Blanke-Baer Chemical Company

1915-1917: F.L. Beggs, The Styron-Beggs Company

1917-1919: F.P. Beers, C.L. Cotton Perfume & Extract Co.

1919-1921: Charles D. Joyce, The A. Colburn Company

1921-1922: Robert E. Heekin, The Heekin Company

1922-1924: Gordon M. Day, Day-Bergwall Company

1924-1926: Fred S. Rogers, McMonagle & Rogers Company

1926-1928: D.T. Gunning, Arbuckle Brothers

1928-1930: George H. Burnett, Joseph Burnett Company

1930-1932: E.L. Brendlinger, The Dill Company

1932-1934: Bernard H. Smith Sr., Virginia Dare Extract Co., Inc.

1934-1936: W.F. Meyer, Warner Jenkinson Company

1936-1938: George M. Armor, McCormick & Company

1938-1939: Leland P. Symmes, Baker Extract Company

1939-1940: Clark E. Davis, Virginia Dare Extract Co., Inc.

1940-1942: John H. Beach, Seeley & Company, Inc.

1942-1944: Lloyd E. Smith, Virginia Dare Extract Co., Inc.

1944-1946: Garret F. Meyer, Warner-Jenkinson Mfg. Company

1946-1947: William B. Durling, Stange Company

1947-1948: George M. Chapman, Liquid Carbonic Corporation

1948-1949: Leslie S. Beggs, The Styron-Beggs Company

1949-1951: John N. Curlett, McCormick & Company

1951-1953: W.G. Grant, National NuGrape Company

1953-1955: William H. Hottinger Jr., Bowey's Inc.

1955-1957: Don C. Jenks, The Foote & Jenks Corporation

1957-1958: Myron J. Hess, S. Twitchell Company

1958-1960: E.N. Heinz Jr., Food Materials Corporation

1960-1962: C.P. McCormick Jr., McCormick & Company

1962-1964: S.M. Kleinschmidt, General Dynamics Corporation

1964-1966: A.S. Wendt, Fred Fear & Company

1966-1968: Howard Smith Sr., Virginia Dare Extract Co., Inc.

1968-1970: Robert H. Pulver, H. Kohnstamm & Company

1970-1972: Richard L. Hall, McCormick & Company

1972-1973: Gene D. Kielhofer, Neumann-Buslee & Wolfe

1973-1974: William T. Miller, Royal Crown Cola Company

1974-1975: Oliver W. Hickel Jr., Warner-Jenkinson Company

1975-1976: Bruce L. Durling, Stange Company

1976-1977: Eugene P. Grisanti, International Flavors & Fragrances Inc.

1977-1978: J. Frank Perkins, Firmenich, Inc.

1978-1979: Robert W. Koch Sr., Food Materials Corporation

1979-1980: John G. Adams, Adams Extract Company

1980-1981: Anthony S. Filandro, Virginia Dare Extract Co., Inc.

1981-1982: Robert M. Hughes, Dragoco

1982-1983: Lewis A. Enkema, Universal Group Limited

1983-1984: J. Allen Brent, The Coca-Cola Company

1984-1985: Ira B. Kapp, Felton International

Presidents

1985-1986: James J. Broderick, H. Kohnstamm & Company, Inc.

1986-1987: William J. Downey Jr., Fritzsche Dodge & Olcott

1987-1988: Robert G. Fries Jr., F&C International, Inc.

1988-1989: Paul F. Hopper, General Foods Corporation

1989-1990: Richard C. Pisano Sr., Citrus and Allied Essences Ltd.

1990-1991: Johannes A. Buchel, PepsiCo

1991-1992: J. Wayne Wheeler, The Foote & Jenks Corporation

1992-1993: James M. Adams, Haarmann & Reimer Corporation

1993-1994: Charles H. Manley, Takasago International Corporation (USA)

1994-1995: James L. Emerson, The Coca-Cola Company

1995-1996: James H. Heinz, Bell Flavors & Fragrances, Inc.

1996-1997: Robert L. Amaducci, Adron, Inc.

1997-1998: Fred H. Stults, Firmenich, Inc.

1998-1999: Daniel E. Stebbins, Dragoco

1999-2000: Arnold L. Manheimer, J. Manheimer, Inc.

2000-2001: Michael E. Davis, Givaudan

2001-2002: Peter N. Lombardo, Robertet, Inc.

2002-2003: Robert H. Leggett, Pepsi-Cola Company

2003-2004: Skip Rosskam, David Michael & Co., Inc.

2004-2005: Stephen A. Block, International Flavors & Fragrances Inc.

2005-2006: Richard C. Pisano Jr., Citrus and Allied Essences Ltd.

2006-2007: Leslie L. Blau, Firmenich, Inc.

2007-2008: Hamed Faridi, McCormick & Company

2008-2009: Howard Smith Jr., Virginia Dare Extract Co., Inc.

Executive Directors

Thomas E. Lannen - 1909-1922

Thomas J. Hickey - 1922-1932

John S. Hall - 1932-1965

Daniel R. Thompson - 1965-2000

Glenn Roberts - 2000-Present

General Counsels

Thomas E. Lannen - 1909-1922

Thomas J. Hickey - 1922-1932

John S. Hall - 1932-1965

Daniel R. Thompson - 1965-2000

John B. Hallagan - 2000-Present

FEMA Expert Panel Members 1960-Present

Anthony A. Ambrose, Ph.D., Medical College of Virginia: 1971-1983

Frank R. Blood, Ph.D., Vanderbilt University School of Medicine: 1969-1970

Samuel M. Cohen, M.D., Ph.D., University of Nebraska Medical Center: 2002-Present

John Doull, M.D., Ph.D., University of Kansas Medical Center: 1978-2003

David W. Fassett, M.D., Eastman Kodak Health and Safety Laboratory: 1960-1983

Victor J. Feron, Ph.D., TNO Nutrition and Food Research Institute: 1999-2006

Horace W. Gerarde, Ph.D., Becton Dickinson & Co.: 1960-1974

Nigel J. Gooderham, Ph.D., Imperial College School of Medicine, University of London: 2009-Present

Jay I. Goodman, Ph.D., Michigan State University: 1997-2005

Lawrence J. Marnett, Ph.D., Vanderbilt University School of Medicine: 2000-Present

Ian Munro, Ph.D., CanTox: 1986-2000

Paul M. Newberne, D.V.M., Ph.D., Boston University School of Medicine: 1979-1999

Bernard L. Oser, Ph.D., Founder and Non-Voting Chairman: 1960-1986

Philip S. Portoghese, Ph.D., University of Minnesota: 1984-Present

Ivonne M.C.M. Rietjens, Ph.D., Wageningen University: 2006-Present

Maurice H. Seevers, M.D., Ph.D., University of Michigan Medical School: 1960-1974

Robert L. Smith, Ph.D., D.Sc., Imperial College School of Medicine, University of London: 1981-Present

Howard C. Spencer, Ph.D., Dow Chemical Biomedical Laboratory: 1960-1984

Jakob A. Stekol, Ph.D., Fels Institute for Cancer Research: 1960-1969

Frank M. Strong, Ph.D., University of Wisconsin: 1970-1976

William J. Waddell, M.D., Ph.D., University of Louisville School of Medicine: 1999-Present

Bernard M. Wagner, M.D., New York University School of Medicine: 1983-2003

Carrol S. Weil, M.A., Bushy Run Research Center: 1981-1998

R. Tecwyn Williams, M.D., Ph.D., University of London St. Mary's Hospital Medical School: 1975-1980

Lauren A. Woods, M.D., Ph.D., Medical College of Virginia: 1960-1998

Table of Contents

Table of Contents

Introduction

People have been using spices and other flavorings to add zest to their food and their lives since well before recorded history. From early times, flavors have been part of a quest to make life more enjoyable and to help make foods and beverages taste better.

Our own native land came to the world's attention because Christopher Columbus sailed off in 1492 to seek a faster route to Far Eastern spice sources. Centuries later, the advent of commercial food processing created the need for flavors that were familiar to consumers yet could be incorporated into the new methods of mass production of food.

Businesses in Germany and Switzerland were the first to expand the market significantly, through the development of synthetic aromatic chemicals that served as the basis of many new artificial flavors. Most of these early commercially produced flavoring substances traced their roots to indigenous ingredients "discovered" by Columbus and other early explorers.

In the United States, many flavor companies began as importers of European essential oils and other flavoring substances. They soon expanded to meet local economic and market needs by formulating and manufacturing ingredients domestically. At the beginning of the 1900s, a growing number of food and beverage companies, including Kellogg, Campbell Soup, Coca-Cola, and Pepsi-Cola, created even more demand for commercial flavors.

Forward-thinking executives of these early U.S. flavor firms recognized the value of joining together to support the growth of the industry. Formalizing their association in the wake of the first Pure Food and Drugs Act of 1906, these early pioneers created the Flavoring Extract Manufacturers' Association (FEMA), the forerunner of today's Flavor and Extract Manufacturers Association, in 1909.

The growing demand for pure, high-quality flavorings helped FEMA quickly evolve into an organization that not only reflected its members' business concerns but also took the lead in protecting consumer interests. Sometimes, FEMA found it necessary to defend the integrity of the industry because its very mystique made it a victim of scurrilous press attacks or widespread misconceptions.

As early as 1914, FEMA could "claim to occupy the important position of being the guardian of the interests of the flavoring extract manufacturing industry of the United States . . . [and] . . . in a position to shape the future course of the extract industry of the country," according to Thomas Lannen, FEMA's first attorney and the first U.S. food and drug lawyer.

And shape the industry FEMA has done over the past 100 years, from formulating standards to fighting unfair taxation to contributing to the 1958 Food Additives Amendment and so much more. Perhaps most notable is the FEMA GRAS program, which has been in the forefront of the concept of using science to demonstrate safety, and has grown to be a globally respected pillar of flavor safety assessment. The association's efforts to promote quality and safety, weed out problem ingredients and help its members protect their valuable trade secrets have become a model of what a trade association can and should be.

FEMA's leadership, its knowledge and awareness of industry trends, and its proactive posture on industry issues have helped its member companies survive and thrive. In an age when consumers focus on healthy eating, counting calories, reducing fat and, as some might say, taking the joy out of food, our industry continues to play a pivotal role by enhancing the experience of eating and drinking through the use of safe and distinctive flavor ingredients.

Comprising more than 100 companies today, many with deep roots in the industry, FEMA continues to provide value for its members and to enlist their expertise and support in developing strategies for the future.

Through its work, FEMA also builds on a sense of common purpose evident from the earliest days of the association. For many of us in this business, FEMA membership is a family tradition, passed from one generation to the next — and as integral a part of operations as product development, production and distribution.

Beginning with my great-grandfather almost 90 years ago, my family has been involved and active in FEMA. In fact, I am proud to note that our company is a fourth-generation FEMA member. My story is not unique — many of my industry colleagues today are descendents of individuals who were prominent in the intertwined history of our industry and FEMA.

FEMA's early operations, characterized by telegrams, hand-typed correspondence and informal meetings of company executives on the docks of New York and New Jersey, have given way to e-mails, workshops and webinars. Yet through a century of change, among newcomers and the old guard, privately held firms and multinationals, companies large and small, one thing about FEMA has remained constant: mutual respect among our members. We cooperate with one another to achieve our association's goals, communicate regularly and have a sense of camaraderie that makes FEMA different, effective — and yes, even fun!

We hope you'll enjoy this peek at the first 100 years of FEMA, gleaned from old storage boxes of dusty correspondence and photos and aided by the memories of longtime FEMA members. Through this book, we honor those who have gone before us and made FEMA an association of which we can be proud. We also salute our current FEMA members, through whose efforts the vision of our early pioneers continues to be implemented now and into the future.

Finally, this book would not have been possible without the help of many individuals. We thank those who gave tirelessly of their time to pull together all the pieces of the past — and to lay the groundwork for the next hundred years.

Howard Smith Jr.
Co-Chair, FEMA 100th Anniversary Committee
FEMA President 2008-2009
President, Virginia Dare Extract Co., Inc.

Chapter 1
1900–1909

The decade that culminated in the formation of the Flavoring Extract Manufacturers' Association** in 1909 began with an increased demand for flavor ingredients. Consumer food and beverage products had been exploding in popularity, and women eagerly embraced the idea of more sophisticated home cooking.

The legendary Fannie Farmer wrote the first edition of the "Boston Cooking-School Cook Book" in 1896, including a then-revolutionary scientific discourse on food chemistry and nutrition to teach homemakers how to nurture their families. Farmer, who had a technical bent, instructed her readers on the availability of almond, vanilla, lemon, orange, peach and rose flavoring extracts "made from the flower, fruit or seed from which they are named." She also pointed her readers to strawberry, pineapple and banana extracts made from fruits or "manufactured from chemicals."

Like home cooks, food companies were also hungry for flavoring components — especially beverage companies. In May 1886, Atlanta, Ga., pharmacist Dr. John Stith Pemberton produced the syrup for Coca-Cola® and carried a jug of the new product down the street to Jacobs' Pharmacy, where it was pronounced "excellent" and placed on sale for 5 cents a glass at the soda fountain. Marriage with carbonated water produced a drink that was "Delicious and Refreshing." The new soft drink created a large demand for flavoring components.

Meanwhile, Caleb Bradham, a pharmacist in New Bern, N.C., was also experimenting with various recipes for a healthful and appealing beverage for his patrons.

FANNIE FARMER Original 1896 BOSTON COOKING-SCHOOL COOK BOOK

The winning formulation was a combination of vanilla, oils and a kola nut extraction the locals called "Brad's drink." Bradham, however, called the drink Pepsi-Cola, perhaps because he thought his product, like pepsin, aided digestion. He incorporated in 1902.

And while McCormick & Company, which got its start in 1889 in Baltimore, Md., is synonymous with spices and flavorings today, it originally sold root beer, fruit syrups and juices along with flavoring extracts. Within a few years, McCormick was successful enough to open an export office in New York City, shipping its products to and from the East and West Indies, South Africa, Europe, and Central and South America.

Around that same time, about a dozen chewing gum manufacturers were doing business in the United States, including the Wrigley family in Chicago.

**The organization formed in 1909 was the Flavoring Extract Manufacturers' Association. This name was used until 1967, when the name was changed to the Flavor and Extract Manufacturers' Association to reflect the growing importance of flavors as distinct from natural extracts. In the mid-1990s, the apostrophe was quietly dropped.

Manufactured by
THE CONSOLIDATED CHICLE COMPANY
JOSEPH GARDNER, President
SEATTLE, WASHINGTON

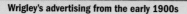

Wrigley's advertising from the early 1900s

In 1891, William Wrigley Jr. arrived in Chicago to sell soap. As an incentive to merchants to carry Wrigley's soap, he offered baking powder as a premium. The baking powder sold better than the soap, so he switched product lines, offering chewing gum as a premium. When the gum proved more popular than the baking powder, Wrigley decided to introduce his own line. The iconic Juicy Fruit®, along with Wrigley's Spearmint® brands, made their debut in 1893.

Only a limited number of essential oils, including mint and citrus, were extracted in the United States in the early 20th century; most essential oils came from French, German, Italian and Swiss flavoring and fragrance houses and were shipped to American companies.

For the fledgling U.S. flavoring companies, the East Side of lower Manhattan near the docks was the ideal place to set up headquarters. It was an easy stroll from an office

Seattle Brewing & Malting Company. *The Argus*, 1900

to meet the boats loaded with raw materials from France and Southeast Asia. Working in close proximity in a two- to three-block area, Dodge & Olcott Company, George Lueders & Company Inc., J. Manheimer and others became as much a fraternity as an industry, with executives of rival companies frequently chatting informally with one another.

These early leaders were responsible for the expansion of the flavoring industry, as more companies developed their own manufacturing processes for extracts. By 1904, Dodge & Olcott had two factories for distillation: one in Brooklyn, N.J., the second in Bayonne, N.J.

Unfortunately, the flavoring boom had also attracted charlatans and triggered the government's concern. "Evidence shows that all peppers, cinnamon, cloves and spices, including ginger and mustard are adulterated," reported a *New York Times* article about a U.S. Senate investigation into food manufacturing practices in the early 1900s. Companies testified that they were reluctant to change, according to the Senate report: "These gentlemen say: 'We would like to quit putting this stuff in coffee, and would be willing to brand our syrups for what they are, but our competitors get a trade advantage which we cannot surrender.'"

After the Senate's meetings, legislators considered several proposals, including putting food products under an Internal Revenue law that previously prohibited filled cheese and adulterated flour, and establishing a new department under the secretary of agriculture that would fix standards for food, beverages and drugs.

Meanwhile, health officials became ever more alarmed. "Era of Adulteration Menaces Public Health," proclaimed a 1904 *New York Times* headline reporting on testimony presented to the American Association for the Advancement of Science. "I am prepared to prove to the satisfaction of any one who will take the trouble to investigate that the greater part of the flavoring extracts offered for sale in the City of New York are made up of various mixtures blended and colored with aniline dyes,"

proclaimed Dr. Leon L. Watters in the *Times* article.

However, it took Upton Sinclair's novel "The Jungle," published in 1906, to create enough outrage among the public to inspire government action. Filled with descriptions of rats being ground into sausages and diseased animals slaughtered for human consumption, "The Jungle" is said to have sickened President Theodore Roosevelt when he read an advance copy, and he urged Congress to pass food safety legislation.

In 1906, after years of debate and proposals, Congress enacted the U.S. Pure Food and Drugs Act, one of the first pieces of legislation to protect American consumers. "One of the wildest times that has been seen this session" is how the *New York Times* described the House events that culminated in a vote of 240 to 17 to approve

continued on page 26

1892

The famous Fig Newton is created.

1899

Millionth gallon of Coca-Cola syrup is produced to satisfy a growing thirst for the soft drink.

Photo courtesy of www.TheCrazedCollector.com

24

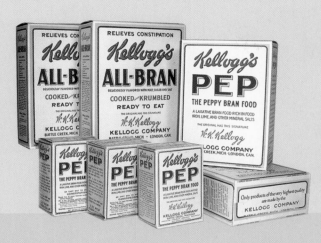

1902

Following the lead of Kellogg and Post, 30 different cereal flake companies spring up in Battle Creek, Mich., to revolutionize breakfast fare.

Patent issued to August Gaulin on July 16 describes how to homogenize milk.

1904

The Campbell Kids are added to Campbell Soup's famous red-and-white can labels.

Mustard begins production at R.T. French Company.

Dr. John S. Pemberton, creator of the original Coca-Cola formula

continued from page 24

the Pure Food and Drugs Act on June 23, 1906. The Senate had passed the measure on Feb. 21.

The whisky issue — whether whisky should be required to carry a label listing the coloring or flavoring ingredients — had fueled a fight among Southern Democrats in the House, watched closely by firms like David Michael & Co., Inc., which got its start in 1896 making whisky in the back room of an Atlantic City, N.J., bar. David Michael's first flavoring agent, known as "Old-time Special Body & Age"®, was a blend of botanicals that made its new whisky taste like 10-year-old bourbon — and the company didn't want to share its ingredients with the world. Fortunately, the proposed

amendment requiring the whisky labeling lost when the House voted to pass the act.

The government's attention turned to enforcement, with Dr. Harvey Wiley, chief chemist in the Bureau of Chemistry at the U.S. Department of Agriculture, heading up the team of enforcement inspectors. Known for his "poison squad" — volunteers who ate food preservatives to test their safety — Wiley crusaded against unsafe foods.

For all of its safety advances, though, the 1906 legislation did not address some issues vital for the flavoring and extract industry as well as for the protection of the American consumer. It did not include language about chemical preservatives, which became a

Some whisky makers touted their products as "guaranteed" under the 1906 Pure Food and Drugs Act.

controversy during Wiley's tenure. Rather than reassuring the public, the Pure Food and Drugs Act sometimes resulted in consumer confusion.

Another complicating factor was the patchwork of inconsistent state laws. A manufacturer could label his product "lemon oil" according to New York labeling law, only to have Florida reject the language.

Responding to this confusion, on Aug. 25, 1909, leading manufacturers met in Cincinnati, Ohio, to form the Flavoring Extract Manufacturers' Association. Willoughby M. McCormick, founder of McCormick & Company, roused the dozen or so attendees to set an ambitious agenda:

- Foster cooperation, promotion and protection of the members' business interests

- Foster and promote good will among the members
- Assist in enacting and enforcing laws that, according to the minutes of that first meeting, "shall deal justly with the rights of flavoring extract manufacturers and consumers."

The founding FEMA members recognized that the quality and safety of ingredients were key to the success of their businesses. This early focus on consumer needs has been an important legacy in FEMA activities even to the present day.

1905

Hydrogenation process invented to keep unsaturated fats from turning rancid. American and British patents issued for proposed use of killing bacteria in food with ionizing radiation.

German-born physicist Albert Einstein publishes his special theory of relativity, challenging views of time and space accepted since Newton's day.

1906

Pure Food and Drugs Act is passed by Congress and signed into law by President Theodore Roosevelt on June 30. Dr. Harvey W. Wiley, a physician and former professor of chemistry at Purdue University, led the charge to establish federal regulations in the food and drug areas as chief chemist of the Bureau of Chemistry at the U.S. Department of Agriculture (a group later to become the Food and Drug Administration).

Upton Sinclair's exposé of poor food handling and adulteration in the meatpacking industry, "The Jungle," leads to the Meat Inspection Act of 1906.

1907

Hershey's KISSES are introduced.

Stephen Babcock begins the so-called single grain experiment at the University of Wisconsin-Madison, testing whether cows can survive on a single type of grain and leading to the development of modern nutritional science.

1908

Agriculture and Food Chemical Division of the American Chemical Society is established.

1909

The Del Monte shield label appears on canned fruits.

First commercially successful plastic, called Bakelite, is invented by Leo Hendrik Baekeland.

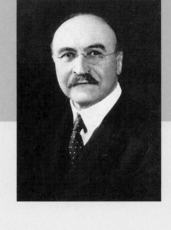

James A. Patten corners the wheat market, driving up the price from 90 cents/bushel to $1.34/bushel.

 The Flavoring Extract Manufacturers' Association is founded.

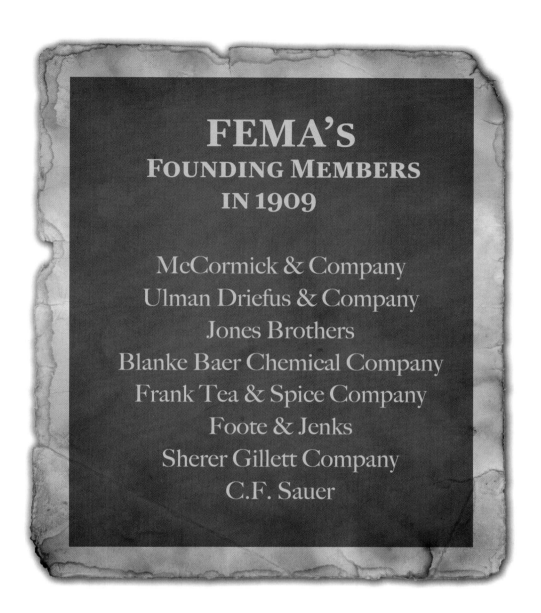

FEMA'S
FOUNDING MEMBERS
IN 1909

McCormick & Company
Ulman Driefus & Company
Jones Brothers
Blanke Baer Chemical Company
Frank Tea & Spice Company
Foote & Jenks
Sherer Gillett Company
C.F. Sauer

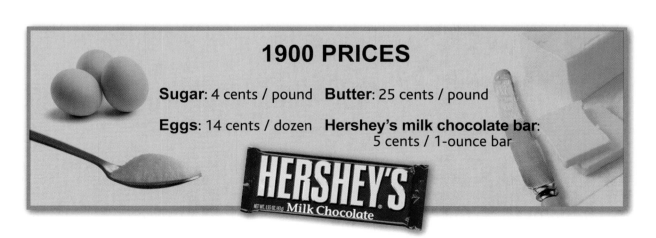

1900 PRICES

Sugar: 4 cents / pound   **Butter:** 25 cents / pound

Eggs: 14 cents / dozen   **Hershey's milk chocolate bar:**
5 cents / 1-ounce bar

31

Chapter 2
1910~1919

I. ULLMANN, 1st V.
R. H. FERGUSON, 3d

A. E. CLAUS, 2d V.
R. S. H. BAER, Secre

RECORD OF MINUTES
of the
First Annual Meeting
of the

FLAVORING EXTRACT
MANUFACTURERS' ASSOCIATION
OF THE UNITED STATES

Held in the Rooms of the Drug and Chemical Club, 100 William Street, New York, June 8-9, 1910.

The decade starting in 1910 was a period of great ferment in the United States as Americans demanded improved working conditions, safer foods and equal rights for women.

It was also a time of great idealism: "Sometimes people call me an idealist. Well, that is the way I know I am an American," President Woodrow Wilson told the nation as the decade came to a close.

Both idealism and a burning desire for change imbued representatives of the flavoring industry when they gathered at New York City's Drug and Chemical Club on June 8- 9, 1910, for the first annual meeting of the fledging Flavoring Extract Manufacturers' Association. Less than a year after the association was organized, it already claimed 74 members in 16 states.

The goal of building an ethical, modern and vital industry could be heard in the address that FEMA President Willoughby M. McCormick gave to the assembled FEMA members.

"Never was there a time when it took men of such capacity to succeed in business; or a time when a manufacturer's or merchant's word stood for more than it does now," said McCormick. "This is the age of commercialism; not selfish, greedy, grasping commercialism, but a broad-gauged liberal and progressive commercialism."

United to protect consumers and support the standards of their industry, the FEMA members were invigorated by new technology but challenged by looming global changes and companies that did not subscribe to their philosophy. Flavoring manufacturers offered support for new federal food and drug legislation. Members deplored unscrupulous companies selling adulterated, misbranded or poisonous products that harmed consumers as well as their industry.

"The Food and Drugs Act of 1906 is a good and substantial foundation upon which to build a model law,"

said one FEMA member at that first annual meeting.

The group also acknowledged that the act created almost as many problems as it alleviated, and they suggested that sections of the law could — and would — be amended. Members were troubled by a lack of uniformity between state and federal food laws. And differences in labeling language were confusing to consumers and costly to members of the flavor industry.

The various rulings also led to skepticism among consumers, who could not be expected to know that flavoring products sold in California might be subject to different regulations than products from Colorado.

Photo courtesy of the National Museum of American History, Behring Center, Smithsonian Institution

I. Ullmann, 1st V. P. W. M. McCormick, President A. E. Claus, 2d V. P.
R. H. Ferguson, 3d V. P. Dr. S. H. Baer, Secretary

BANQUET AT THE HOTEL KNICKERBOCKER, NEW YORK, JUNE 9, 1910.

FEMA 1910 annual meeting

Food safety pioneer Harvey Wiley was immortalized in a 1956 postage stamp.

Coordinating state and federal regulations was one of the first orders of business for FEMA. Members drew up a list of questions for various state pure food commissioners as well as for the U.S. Department of Agriculture. Thanks to FEMA's efforts, manufacturers at last could learn which states were in agreement with the national pure food law, and which had special regulations companies had to meet.

At the same time FEMA members were urging uniformity, they lobbied against frivolous legislation, such as a proposed Maryland bill to require manufacturers to attach bells to poisons including laudanum and paregoric, presumably to get consumers' attention. It is worth noting, however, that the 1906 act did not prohibit such substances — including opium, cocaine and chloroform — from being in foods; it merely required that, if present, the foods be so labeled.

While FEMA worked to address the shortcomings of the Pure Food and Drugs Act during the decade, its members also faced the pressures of taxes on alcoholic ingredients. U.S. companies paid a tax ($2.07 a gallon) on the alcohol they used to create products for export. This put American companies exporting to Europe at a disadvantage compared with English, German and French firms that did not pay alcohol taxes.

Changing the alcohol tax laws became another priority for FEMA during its first annual meeting, as leadership argued that eliminating the tax would benefit consumers as well as manufacturers.

Working with the legislative branch of government, though, was only part of the agenda at early FEMA meetings; thanks to the open and cooperative efforts of FEMA organizers, members learned about new technology from the leading businesses in the flavoring industry.

"There is at least three times as much vanilla consumed as of all other flavors together, and in all probability the consumer knows less of its origin than of any other material from which extracts are made," according to Dr. E.M. Chace, chief assistant to Dr. Harvey Wiley with the U.S. Department of Agriculture.

Their interest piqued, FEMA members participated in a vanilla bean seminar, learning about vanilla bean

continued on page 40

35

1910

Sir Ernest Rutherford undertakes research work that enables him to construct the first nuclear model of the atom, a cornerstone of present-day physics.

1912

Louis-Camille Maillard first proposes that flavor compounds may be formed at high temperatures, the beginning of our understanding of the pathway that forms the basis for many of today's processed flavors.

George Washington Carver demonstrates the value of peanuts and sweet potatoes in fixing nitrogen in the soil to help fertilize it.

1912

Ice cream sales hit 30 million gallons, up from 5 million gallons at the turn of the century.

Tea appears in small China silk bags made by tea importer Thomas Sullivan.

Cookie lovers rejoice when the National Biscuit Company introduces the first Oreo Biscuits.

37

1912

Hellman's Blue Ribbon Mayonnaise is first produced commercially, a breakthrough in emulsion use that formed the foundation of the salad dressing industry.

1914

Frank Van Camp rolls out canned tuna. When albacore tuna later disappears from the San Diego area in 1926, he uses the darker, yellowfin tuna and calls it Chicken of the Sea.

1917

James L. Kraft supplies the first processed cheese to the U.S. military, grinding cheese products and making an emulsion with added water, then forming into loaves of cheese.

The United States enters World War I.

1919

The Treaty of Versailles is signed, officially ending World War I.

But even though the federal government approved its use, several states banned the preservative, providing another challenge for FEMA.

As mentioned in the previous chapter, beverage making, which had been a home kitchen art, soon became the province of industrial production, thanks to the success of Coca-Cola, Pepsi-Cola and other soft drink companies in the golden age of mass-produced beverages. In Columbus, Ga., pharmacist Claud A. Hatcher concocted his own soft drinks in the basement of the family's food business. In 1905 Hatcher introduced Union Bottle Works, which eventually became known as Royal Crown Company Inc. In 1912 the company was renamed Chero-Cola Company, for its cola drink.

With their specific formulations, the new soft drink companies inspired greater flavoring variety in the industry.

This wasn't just the soft drink decade, though: With its distinctive hole in the middle, the Life Saver Mint was introduced in 1913. But the candy, which used volatile peppermint flavoring, almost failed. As the company discovered, the mint flavoring quickly escaped from the candy, leaving it with a flat taste. With the simple solution of wrapping each roll of candies in foil, the flavor remained strong and sales grew.

The Wrigley Company, which introduced its first chewing gum in 1893, expanded its line to include Doublemint® gum in 1914.

Tougher times lay ahead in the second half of the decade as World War I, the Great War, created severe hardships for soft drink companies.

continued from page 35

cultivation, processing and extraction along with the emerging synthetic vanillin. No aspect of the flavoring process, from possible improvements in oil of cloves to the best quality cork closures, was too insignificant for discussion during annual meetings.

Early in the 20th century, FEMA members were also eager to modernize food preservation technology, ending seasonal limitations for ingredients. Members already knew about food drying, canning, refrigeration and "antiseptic" preservation, defined as preserving with salt, sugar, vinegar or alcohol. But each method was limited in its ability to maintain a fresh, wholesome product.

The U.S. government tested and approved sodium benzoate for human use, and FEMA members learned about its virtues as a preservation compound. FEMA member scientists experimented with sodium benzoate and recommended it to prevent fermentation in fresh fruit.

Photo courtesy of www.luckeycards.com

40

Photo courtesy of Drummond's Pictorial Atlas of North Carolina

When the United States entered the war in 1917, sugar rationing and price controls limited soft drink production.

Pepsi-Cola creator Caleb Bradham couldn't find enough sugar to meet the demand for his soft drink, and his efforts to substitute other sweeteners met with consumer disapproval. In the early 1920s Pepsi-Cola declared bankruptcy (the company has been resurrected more than once). The Chero-Cola Company struggled against the sugar shortage by purchasing raw sugar from Cuba and operating its own refinery. But after commanding a premium price during the war, sugar's price dropped sharply by 1920, leaving Chero-Cola battered.

The sugar shortage during World War I was not as grave a concern for the flavoring industry as it was for soft drink manufacturers, as companies could substitute granulated corn sugar for cane sugar in many formulations. Taxes and the growing national interest in prohibition, which was building during the decade, caused more worry.

Members of FEMA feared the effect of proposed government war taxes on

alcohol and extracts. Reporting at the 1917 annual meeting, experts predicted taxes on alcohol could double. They also estimated a 12-cent-per-gallon jump in taxes for the finished extract. Almost certainly, much of the support for "war taxes" on alcohol came from those who favored prohibition and considered taxes a desirable though temporary first step.

FEMA leaders successfully worked to make sure wartime legislation didn't keep members from procuring essential ingredients, and to prevent members from being "indirectly taxed out of existence by taxes placed on raw materials which we use," said Thomas Lannen, FEMA's first attorney, speaking at the 1918 annual meeting.

The drive toward prohibition was coming from several fronts, including women's social reform groups and patriotic organizations arguing that grain should be turned into bread for fighting men, not into liquor. A wartime prohibition act was enacted for that reason. FEMA watched as state after state stopped alcohol sales in the years before the Eighteenth Amendment was ratified in 1919.

Again, FEMA lobbied to protect its members from the threat of laws that banned flavoring extracts simply because they contained alcohol and were considered

Proof of Chero-Cola popularity is found wherever bottled soft drinks are sold. Everywhere, you see one person after another enjoying Chero-Cola in the Twist Bottle.

The Chero-Cola Bottling Co.
Chas. S. Mosey, Prop.
82 E. Fifth St.   Mansfield, O.
Canal 1608

Chero-Cola
In the *twist* bottle

possible substitutes for alcoholic beverages.

In 1918 alone, the FEMA legislative committee wrote 1,709 opinions and reports covering almost 900 state and federal prohibition bills. In 1919, after the Eighteenth Amendment had been ratified but before legislation was passed to enforce it, FEMA members sent their congressmen telegrams stating: "We call your attention to the fact that all prohibition bills now before Congress as worded would destroy our legitimate business . . ."

FEMA members' hard work paid off in October 1919: When the National Prohibition Act (the "Volstead Act") was passed to enable enforcement of the Eighteenth Amendment, flavoring extracts were exempted if declared non-potable, or unfit for beverage use. The United States' great experiment with Prohibition had begun.

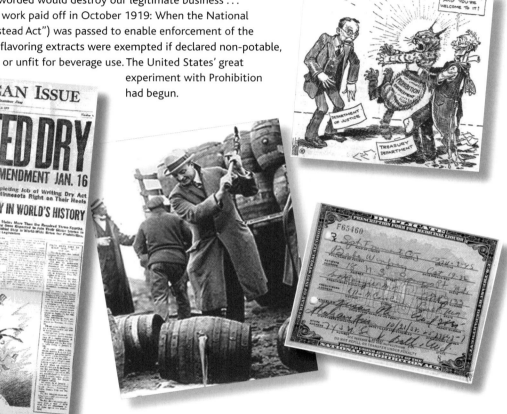

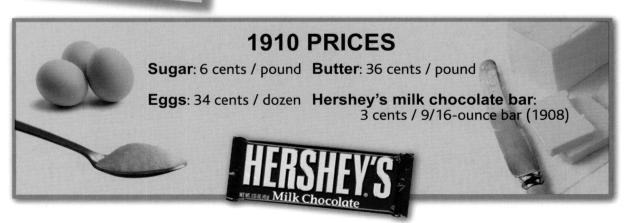

1910 PRICES

Sugar: 6 cents / pound **Butter**: 36 cents / pound

Eggs: 34 cents / dozen **Hershey's milk chocolate bar:**
3 cents / 9/16-ounce bar (1908)

Chapter 3
1920~1929

Frigidaire
Frozen Delights

Frigidaire
Frozen Delights

As Prohibition roared into 1920s America, FEMA's biggest issue of the decade was the ever-changing regulations controlling the use of ethyl alcohol and the distribution of flavoring products. As a result of the resources, vigor and foresight that FEMA devoted to meeting these regulatory challenges, the group would emerge as one of the leading trade organizations in the country.

A key part of FEMA's early operating philosophy was to invite speakers from regulatory agencies to its meetings, beginning in 1920 with James Caffrey, the former head of the Legal Division of the Prohibition Unit of the Internal Revenue Bureau. These speakers attended nearly all meetings of the association throughout the decade, creating a positive and beneficial dialogue.

"I believe the department at Washington feels that it

is perfectly safe in leaving the regulation of flavoring extracts in your own hands, and you know from the regulations . . . that we practically depended on your own good faith," Caffrey said, summing up his division's thoughts on potability determinations.

FEMA earned this respect as a self-regulated organization by taking such steps as establishing a Vigilance Committee in 1921. The committee's role was to monitor the adoption of ways and means to prevent the improper use of flavoring extracts in violation of Prohibition. Because states had their own regulations, a FEMA representative was assigned to each state to monitor and advocate for the flavor industry.

That oversight included not only state regulations but restrictions by individual cities as well. For example, both Canton and Youngstown, Ohio, attempted to pass city ordinances confining sales of all items that contained alcohol to drugstores — thereby preventing general merchants from selling flavor extracts if the products contained more than one-half of one percent alcohol. The FEMA Legislative Committee learned of the move by Canton in time to take action, but the Youngstown ordinance was approved.

FEMA played an active role in federal oversight of Prohibition by participating in the Prohibition Commissioner's Industrial Advisor's Council, made up of staff members from companies that used industrial and non-beverage alcohol in their manufacturing processes. Fred Rogers of McMonagle & Rogers, Middletown, N.Y., served as FEMA's first representative on the council.

Covering all of its bases, FEMA also led the drive to develop a substitute for ethyl alcohol in the manufacture of flavoring extracts for all uses.

At the annual FEMA meeting in 1922, the Research Committee reported on a resolution adopted by FEMA active and associate member chemists, calling for the continued investigation into a "satisfactory substitute" for ethyl alcohol and requesting that "suggestions and assistance be invited from all chemists."

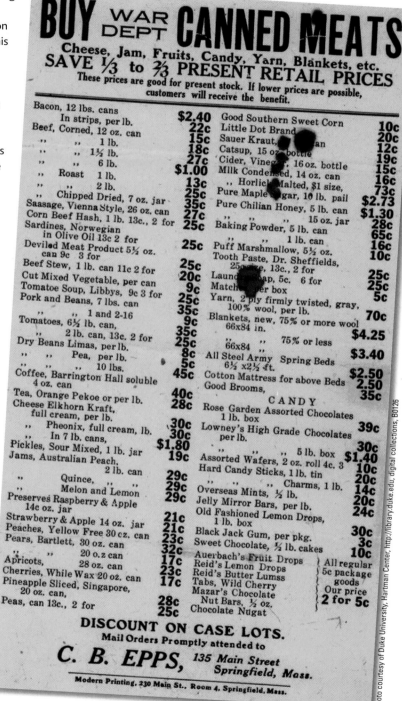

TESTED
RECIPES WITH

Blue Ribbon
Malt Extract

With its wide outreach to both government and industry during the Prohibition years, FEMA's efforts helped the flavor industry stay alive and continue to grow despite the limitations of alcohol restrictions.

Beyond Prohibition, other new federal food regulations continued to emerge during the 1920s. In 1923, the U.S. Bureau of Chemistry published new food standards that included flavor extracts. The standards focused on extract labels, paying particular attention to vanilla. FEMA did not agree with the new standards and spent much of the remainder of the decade analyzing and defining them.

For instance, FEMA argued that the law could not compel a flavor manufacturer to include an ingredient list or the words "artificial flavor and color" on a product already labeled as "imitation."

continued on page 51

Photo courtesy of The Granger Collection, New York

Photo courtesy of The Granger Collection, New York

1923

Clarence Birdseye opens Birds Eye Seafood in New York City, using his patented freezing process. The operation is a bust, but he continues to improve the process and opens General Seafood (which later becomes part of General Foods) in Gloucester, Mass., in 1924.

1924

Food fortification begins with the introduction of table salt fortified with iodine to prevent goiter, a disease caused by lack of iodine in the diet.

1927

Nebraska inventor Edwin Perkins concocts Kool-Aid, selling it in six flavors: strawberry, cherry, lemon-lime, grape, orange, and raspberry.

48

IMITATION GRAPE FLAVORED

KOOL-AID

BASE FOR SOFT DRINKS AND DESSERTS • USE WITH SUGAR

ORIGINAL

NET WEIGHT

1½ OUNCES

1929

The Agricultural Marketing Act of 1929 helps farmers form cooperatives and share some costs of farming.

Wax-coated milk cartons make their way into the growing number of home refrigerators.

Photo courtesy of www.dairyantiques.com

Standard Brands (later to be acquired by Nabisco) is formed from Chase and Sanborn (coffee), Fleischmann's (yeast) and Royal Baking Powder Co. (gelatin desserts).

The stock market crashes in October, starting the cycle of events that culminate in the Great Depression of the 1930s.

Wholesome desserts *can*
be delicious

Many new and valuable suggestions for the use of Burnett's Vanilla will be found in the 5th revised edition of "Dainty and Artistic Desserts." Send for it. Enclose your grocer's name and 15c in stamps or coin to cover mailing.

HOW eagerly children greet the appearance of a dessert they like. Yet how often they have to be coaxed to eat the plain, nourishing puddings that are such an essential part of their diet. "Eat it, dear, because it's good for you," may be an excellent reason for forcing a child to eat a thing; but how much better for the child if it really enjoys doing so. Children's tastes are just as sensitive as our own. They like to eat things that appeal to their taste and do not care for things that lack flavor.

It is a simple matter, however, to give the most ordinary dessert a delightful flavor, if one only knows the secret of Burnett's Vanilla. Its mellow, flowerlike fragrance appeals to the natural taste of children just as surely as it gratifies the more cultivated taste of grown-ups. Then too, the guaranteed purity of Burnett's Vanilla assures you of its healthfulness, as well as "full flavor."

Be sure to tell your grocer "Burnett's."

JOSEPH BURNETT CO.   BOSTON, MASS.

Burnett's Vanilla
Since 1847~Burnett's extracts have meant full flavor

Photo courtesy of the Southborough Historical Society, www.southboroughhistory.org

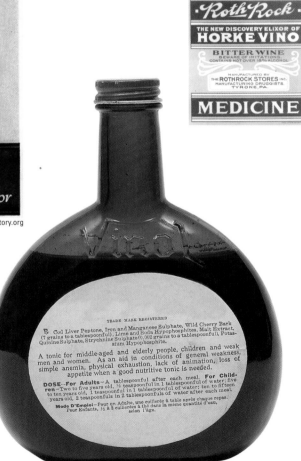

continued from page 47

"When it is plainly labeled as an imitation, that label covers the whole ground and there is neither law nor reason for compelling any further or supplemental statement," according to a FEMA circular issued on April 16, 1923, covering new Bureau of Chemistry regulations.

Vanilla extract labeling encompassed one of the major issues of the decade: the development of a vanilla standard of identity. FEMA spent a great deal of effort gathering data on vanilla to establish the groundwork for a standard of identity, much of it spearheaded by Dr. Frank M. Boyles of McCormick & Company. "When some chemist compounds a synthetic vanilla extract, the flavor of which perfectly imitates that of vanilla, we shall acclaim him a genius... but until then, let us jealously guard for the benefit of the public and ourselves the sacredness of the label, 'Pure Extract of Vanilla,'" Boyles said.

The 1920s also saw the groundwork laid for the "drawback system," which enabled flavor manufacturers to "draw back" all but one dollar of tax paid on a beverage alcohol used in flavors.*

In 1926, FEMA's Legislative Committee fought for and helped win a reduction in the tax on alcohol that members paid, leading to 25 percent decreases in both 1927 and 1928. FEMA President Rogers praised the committee for "[carrying] on the battle loyally and valiantly" as the Senate wavered on the tax reduction during the final days before its passage. FEMA had campaigned to reduce the alcohol tax since 1915, when it accounted for 30 percent of the cost of vanilla extract and 70 percent of the cost of lemon extract. The association emphasized the unfairness of taxing articles of domestic production that were used in the manufacturing of other products.

The growing sophistication of the flavor industry throughout the decade helped contribute to its growth. By 1925, the industry comprised 433 companies with total revenues of more than $94 million, according to a U.S. Department of Commerce report. One of FEMA's goals during this time was to help the industry increase its sales through a variety of education efforts.

FEMA also looked at ways to collect and share information on various aspects of the flavor business, information that could help the industry grow. For example, for many years the association issued reports summarizing the approximate costs and availability

*Editor's note: The law has caused significant administrative complexity over the years, and compliance costs have increased. However, FEMA's hard work in the 1920s and the 1930s creating this system paid off. In 2008, the tax per proof gallon was set at $13.50. Without the drawback system, flavor manufacturers might well have paid the full beverage tax. Stabilizing the net fee for nearly 100 years has saved the industry tens of millions of dollars.

Maurice Maubert took over operations at Robertet in 1923.

FEMA members at the 1927 annual meeting

JELL-O *America's most famous Dessert*

Little Jack Horner sat in a corner
What can the reason be?
Indeed it's quite plain
He is hiding from Jane.
For a big dish of JELL-O has he

Wesson Oil

SALADS COOKING

A PURE RICH VEGETABLE FAT
for frying shortening and salad dressings
ALL IN ONE HANDY CAN
Pints, Quarts Half-gallons and Gallons

of various components of extracts and other flavor products. In addition, FEMA worked to discourage the sale of adulterated and misbranded products by disreputable manufacturers who would substitute cheap — and sometimes dangerous — substances for safe and wholesome ingredients. These companies would "accept business at almost any price," according to the minutes of the 1922 annual meeting.

In fact, FEMA helped members with nearly every aspect of their business. One of the most worrisome during the 1920s was transportation. Railroad classification committees were debating thousands of classification proposals that threatened to have a big impact on the industry's bottom line. Throughout the decade, FEMA's Transportation Committee closely monitored the regulations and freight rates, speaking for its members when necessary.

The government and the business community were not the only audiences for flavor education during the decade. The industry recognized that it was critical to promote the importance of flavors to consumers too. FEMA embarked on several campaigns aimed at the public, promoting the role of flavor in a well-balanced diet. "Educational news publicity," presented in an impartial manner through the nation's newspapers, provided an ideal method for FEMA to launch an awareness campaign on pure vanilla in 1929.

"The main objective will be 'flavor-consciousness,' the building up of a greater and more widespread desire for the use of our products in the daily menu of American homes," the association reported. The vanilla campaign not only engendered goodwill for flavoring extracts in general, but also helped to turn casual newspaper readers — including hundreds of thousands of American homemakers — into potential customers.

The New York Stock Exchange in 1929

paid secretary be appointed by the president for the first time.

As FEMA approached its 20th anniversary in 1929, it had begun to focus more on meeting attendance and membership growth. In 1928 FEMA launched a membership drive, with Membership Committee Chairman Leslie Talmadge of Williams & Carleton Company writing to existing members to ask for references: "Your Executive Committee is making a serious study of the problems of our industry, such as packages, closures, raw material fluctuations, costs, tendencies in distribution, et cetera — all good constructive work and affecting our entire membership. In order to make this work more effective we must have a larger membership."

While FEMA was advocating on the national stage, it was also building its organization from the inside out, establishing an infrastructure that would serve it well for decades. The association began the 1920s by doubling member dues from $25 to $50, a move that would help it pay for such business expenses as travel (a whopping $1,996.36 for the year ending June 1, 1920), stenographers ($737.89), postage ($249.60), and telegrams ($41.06). The Executive Committee also recommended that a

With the crash of the stock market in October 1929 and the beginning of the economic slide that led to the Great Depression, FEMA's members looked to their greater numbers for strength as they prepared to face the new economic realities of the 1930s.

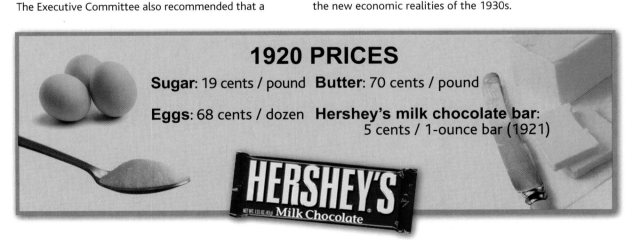

1920 PRICES

Sugar: 19 cents / pound **Butter**: 70 cents / pound

Eggs: 68 cents / dozen **Hershey's milk chocolate bar**: 5 cents / 1-ounce bar (1921)

Chapter 4
1930-1939

The New York Times.

LATE CITY EDITION

VOL. LXXXIII...No. PLPA.   NEW YORK, WEDNESDAY, DECEMBER 6, 1933.   TWO CENTS

LINDBERGHS AT SEA ON BRAZIL FLIGHT; 'O.K.' SHE REPORTS

TAX PLAN OFFERED TO CURB EVASIONS, RAISE $237,000,000

PROHIBITION REPEAL IS RATIFIED AT 5:32 P.M.; ROOSEVELT ASKS NATION TO BAR THE SALOON; NEW YORK CELEBRATES WITH QUIET RESTRAINT

Photo courtesy of The Granger Collection, New York

The 1930s were difficult years for the United States, with the Great Depression casting millions into poverty and another world war on the horizon amid ominous murmurs of conflict in Europe and Asia. The repeal of Prohibition in 1933 under President Franklin D. Roosevelt was a bright spot for many. But as America prepared for war, and government spending increased, Congress looked toward new taxes for revenue. Alcohol, so important to the flavor industry as a solvent and carrier, once again became an easy target. In the food and beverage industry, distribution advances were starting to change the way products were

Photo courtesy of The Granger Collection, New York

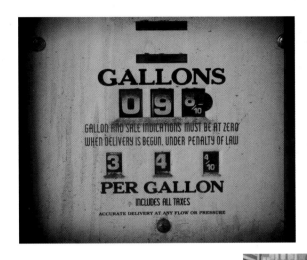

made available to consumers. All of these events had a significant impact on FEMA and the course the association charted through the decade.

When the stock market crashed in 1929, the aftershocks were felt throughout lower Manhattan, where virtually all of the great American flavor houses were located. While business had boomed as the Roaring '20s concluded, no one could have imagined the economic carnage that would come with the 1930s.

Take the case of Star Extract Works, founded in the 1890s by David Katzenstein, a German immigrant who arrived in the United States in 1870. Katzenstein's flavor extract company prospered and expanded through the years, and in 1928 it moved from Manhattan to a new four-building manufacturing complex in the open fields of the Bronx. Even though Katzenstein hadn't made a significantly bad business decision in 38 years, the expansion slammed to a

Photo courtesy of The Granger Collection, New York

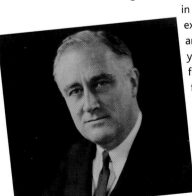

President Franklin D. Roosevelt

First Lady Eleanor Roosevelt

57

halt with the stock market crash. He was forced to sell three of the buildings at a loss and barely hung on to the primary manufacturing facility. Times became so dire that at one point the company rejoiced at selling a single gallon of vanilla.

With the economy in freefall, FEMA confronted several major issues as the 1930s began, starting with federal government oversight. "We are faced with one of the most momentous changes that has taken place in our relationship with our government since the passage of the Volstead Act," said FEMA President George H. Burnett of the Joseph Burnett Company at the association's 1930 annual meeting. The change he referred to was the transfer of control of non-beverage alcohol from the Treasury Department to the Department of Justice as provided by the Williamson Bill.

FEMA had strenuously protested certain sections of the bill, arguing that it would be in the best interests of everyone to keep industrial alcohol oversight in the hands of the Treasury Department. That agency was well-acquainted with the association's stance and had drawn up the industrial alcohol regulations after extensive conferences between the Prohibition Bureau and the industry. FEMA argued — to no

MAKE PERFECT ICE CREAM AT HOME THIS EASY*WAY!

*4 Minutes to Prepare

SIMPLY MIX

FREEZE

and SERVE

The best ice cream you ever tasted, frozen right in your ice tray with milk, cream, and Burnett's Liquid-Mix. It's delicious, with a perfect texture and flavor, because Liquid-Mix is *made by Burnett* — known for 90 years as the manufacturers of Burnett's Pure Vanilla, a real quality product familiar to millions of housewives.

YOUR CHILD'S FAVORITE DESSERT. Every one knows that ice cream is childhood's favorite dessert—a real event at any time! Always keep an ice tray full. Have it ready for youngsters coming home from school. They love it and be-

cause Liquid-Mix is made by Burnett, you know it's good for them.

FIVE GOOD FLAVORS. Every one is a pure flavor, and whenever vanilla is used, it's Burnett's. Here they are: Vanilla, Chocolate, Strawberry, Maple, and Orange-Pineapple.

FOUR SHERBETS, TOO, FOR REAL ECONOMY. With any one of the four Burnett Sherbets (Raspberry, Lemon, Pineapple or Orange), you can make nearly a quart of this delicious and cooling summer dessert for about 10 1/3 cents

— 10 cents for the can of sherbet, the rest for water and a little sugar. Burnett's Sherbets can be made with milk or water, and are also delicious made with condensed or evaporated milk.

PERFECT FOR HAND FREEZERS. If you like to freeze your ice cream in the good old-fashioned way, Burnett's Liquid-Mix was made to order for you. No cooking, no hulling or washing berries, just mix according to directions and put in the freezer in the regular way.

For one Liquid-Mix label and 10 cents we'll send you this VALUABLE SPOON. Heavy Silver Plate, specially designed for ice cream and frozen desserts. Fully guaranteed by R. Wallace & Sons of Wallingford, Conn. Have fair retail value of $3 a dozen.

BURNETT'S
Liquid-Mix
ICE CREAM
STRAWBERRY

BURNETT'S
Liquid-Mix
10¢
at your grocer's
Made by the Makers of Burnett's Pure Vanilla

JOSEPH BURNETT COMPANY, Dept. A
437 D Street, Boston, Mass.

I enclose_____Liquid-Mix labels and_____cents for
_____heavy silver plate ice cream spoons.

Name_____
Address_____
City_____State_____

During the 1930 annual meeting, FEMA members toured the White House.

and combinations to make soft drinks taste good, appealing to consumers looking for an affordable treat. Coca-Cola, Pepsi-Cola, Hires Root Beer, A&W Root Beer, Seven-Up, Dr Pepper and others produced a remarkably steady income — even in hard times — as they capitalized on advancements in production, bottling, and expanded distribution to broaden the beverage market.

avail — that not only was the attorney general unfamiliar with this branch of law, but it would be confusing and laborious to cancel the current regulations and have the Department of Justice draw up new ones.

Prohibition remained a dangerous threat to the flavor industry until it was repealed in 1933. Although the repeal was cause for relief, the unreasonably high taxes on non-beverage alcohol and the debate over what constituted an "unfit beverage" that allowed for tax rebates were still crucial discussion points for the industry. Extract manufacturers were taxed $2.25 per proof gallon in the 1930s, and some observers predicted the tax could go as high as $4 in the future, creating an enormous burden for the industry.

While Prohibition and its repeal had focused attention on alcoholic beverages, a new market for soft drinks was exploding across the nation, providing opportunities for flavor manufacturers struggling to remain profitable during the Depression. Companies experimented with new flavors

The end of Prohibition also ushered in an opportunity for manufacturers to create new flavors. W. Sheinker & Son of New York City advertised a line of liquor flavors such as rye extract, gin extract, and crème de cacao extract, all designed to be used to make liquors and cordials for home consumption. "It is our intention to advertise these flavors to the public in general, suggesting to them that liquors, for personal use, can be made at home if mixed

continued on page 64

1930

Unilever is created from the merger of British soap maker Lever Brothers and Dutch margarine producer Margarine Unie, an international union that was unusual at the time.

The name of the Food, Drug, and Insecticide Administration is shortened to Food and Drug Administration under an agricultural appropriations act.

McNary-Mapes Amendment authorizes FDA standards of quality and fill-of-container for canned food, excluding meat and milk products.

1930-31

First of the four major droughts of the decade covers virtually the entire Plains, damaging crops with deficient rainfall, high temperatures and high winds, as well as insect infestations and dust storms.

1933

KNOTT'S BERRY FARM

Walter Knott serves up boysenberry jam made by his farm/company, Knott's Berry Farm.

Richard Kuhn and Dr. Paul György begin collaborating on research into the B vitamins, and become the first to isolate and purify vitamin B2 (riboflavin).

1934

Modern freeze-drying process (quick-freezing followed by drying under high vacuum conditions at a low temperature) is patented.

Pet Milk Company introduces evaporated milk fortified with vitamin D by irradiation.

1935

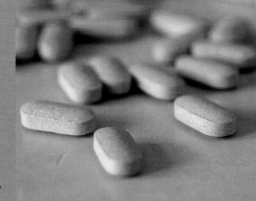

Robert R. Williams first reports the chemical composition and synthesis of vitamin B1 (thiamine).

Vitamin C becomes the first vitamin to be artificially synthesized.

1938

The 1938 Food, Drug, and Cosmetic Act is passed by Congress, authorizing standards of identity, quality and fill-of-container for foods.

1939

The first federal food standards are issued, for canned tomatoes, tomato puree and tomato paste.

The Institute of Food Technologists is formed after a meeting at MIT attended by 600 people, with MIT Prof. Samuel C. Prescott serving as the group's first president.

Photo courtesy of Duke University, Hartman Center, http://library.duke.edu, digital collections, MM0081

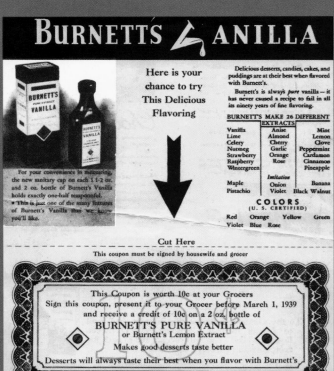

Photo courtesy of the Southborough Historical Society, www.southboroughhistory.org

continued from page 59

directly with tax-paid alcohol," W. Sheinker wrote in a letter to FEMA in 1934. "In our opinion, products of this type, advertised that way, would not conflict with the Federal Laws inasmuch as we mention 'tax-paid alcohol,' and, in this way, the Government obtains their full revenue."

Even as the restraints of Prohibition were being relaxed, the federal government turned its attention to regulation in other areas. By 1933, the Food and Drug Administration had recommended a complete revision of the 1906 Food and Drugs Act, launching a five-year legislative battle that culminated in the 1938 Food, Drug, and Cosmetic Act. The new act mandated the institution of standards of identity for certain foods. This movement toward food standards during the 1930s helped launch FEMA's vanilla research effort to explore standards for vanilla products such as vanilla extract and other vanilla formulations. During Prohibition, a growing market had developed for imitation vanilla in the absence of any standards. In many cases, companies marketed "vanilla extracts" that contained only trace amounts of vanilla extract. (FEMA played a leading role in helping guide the long-term effort to develop a federal standard for vanilla products, resulting in the eventual adoption of a standard by the FDA in the 1960s.)

The federal government was also becoming more proactive in workplace issues during the 1930s as the Great Depression took its toll on employment. By the time FEMA celebrated its silver anniversary at the

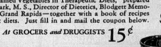

Waldorf-Astoria Hotel in New York City in 1934, the association had begun to develop its own code for members in anticipation of the 1933 National Recovery Act's voluntary code covering wages, hours and trade practices.

Many FEMA members filled out questionnaires covering the major points in the proposed code, including average work hours and salaries. A look back shows that office workers, plant workers and shipping clerks earned $23 per week, while superintendents were compensated at the lofty rate of $41. FEMA also studied industry practices like rebates, cooperative advertising, and credit on returned goods.

As times and economic conditions changed during the 1930s, FEMA worked hard to stay in the forefront of new business practices. After dinner and a lecture at the 1931 annual convention by Dr. Ernest Guenther, chief research chemist of Fritzsche Brothers, Inc. and the world authority on essential oils, FEMA members were treated to a new audiovisual experience: a film about the vanilla industry. Was this film entertainment, or business, or both? Regardless, it was one of the first times the association would use a new form of media to communicate its message to members and the world at large.

From newfangled motion pictures to old-fashioned federal regulations, FEMA's willingness to work not only with its members but also with the government enhanced its stature and attracted attention from other trade associations. "Flavor manufacturers are fortunate indeed in having an association so alive to the requirements of the industry," reported the *American Perfumer and Essential Oil Review* in its July 1933 issue. "It should hardly be necessary to point out to manufacturers who are not yet members that the FEMA is working for them and that membership is almost an obligation."

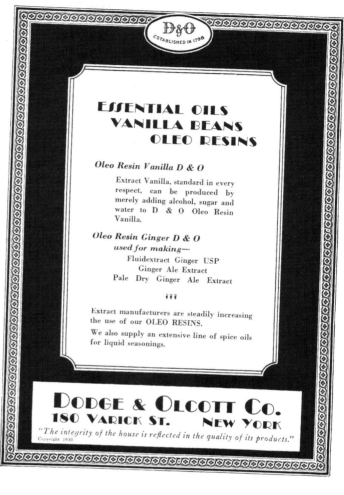

Photo courtesy of The Granger Collection, New York

1930 PRICES

Sugar: 6 cents / pound **Butter**: 46 cents / pound

Eggs: 45 cents / dozen **Hershey's milk chocolate bar**: 5 cents / 2-ounce bar

Chapter 5
1940~1949

The 1940s presented the flavor industry with a unique set of challenges originating with both national and world events. The FEMA Science Committee had spent the 1930s doing major research to create a standard for vanilla extract, but much work remained. The alcohol tax issue had not been resolved to the satisfaction of the industry. FEMA members felt that extracts and flavors should be treated like food products, with ethanol not taxed like potable alcohol.

Against this backdrop, war was raging in Europe and the Far East. Rationing and the scarcity of raw materials from around the world made a great impact on businesses, with prices soaring for both commodity items and essential oil and flavor ingredients — when they were available.

When the 1938 Food, Drug, and Cosmetic Act took full effect on July 1, 1940, the Food and Drug Administration let it be known that its small staff was already overwhelmed with higher-priority work — and if the industry wanted a change in standards, it was up to FEMA to provide the impetus. While FEMA supported the new act, which was designed to safeguard public health and prevent the distribution of misbranded or adulterated products, the association argued that the new law must be carefully applied in order to protect the trade secrets, particularly the production processes, of its members.

A prodigious output of other state legislation also kept FEMA busy at the beginning of the decade. According to a report by FEMA attorney John S. Hall at the 1941 annual meeting, the association had been inundated with more than 1,400 state and federal bills during the 1940-41 legislative period of Congress. New York (104) and California (92) were the most active, but virtually every state in the union had passed

FEMA attorney John S. Hall

Photo courtesy of *The American Perfumer and Essential Oil Review*, 1944

some form of legislation that potentially could affect members of the flavor industry.

The continuing legislative battle over unreasonably high taxes on alcohol was also a major issue for FEMA during the 1940s. The tax had risen to $4 per proof gallon by 1941, almost double what it had been just a few years earlier. At the 1941 annual meeting, the membership voted to send a resolution to Congress regarding the alcohol tax issue. While recognizing that raising taxes for national defense was imperative, FEMA deplored the fact that Congress had failed to establish a tax differential between beverage and non-beverage alcohol, such as that used for medicinal and food purposes. The association resolved, "That it is our earnest hope that the Congress at its next session, in framing tax legislation, will give most serious consideration to the establishment of this tax differential, in order to give relief to the medicinal and food industries whose products are necessities in every American home."

After the Alcohol Tax Reduction Committee lobbied Congress in earnest for relief — with the full support of the membership — FEMA celebrated a partial victory

Officers of F.E.M.A. for 1949-50

John N. Curlett
President

Frank D. Nowland
1st Vice-President

W. G. Grant
2nd Vice-President

Wm. H. Hottinger Jr.
3rd Vice-President

L. P. Symmes
Secretary

Lloyd E. Smith
Treasurer

John S. Hall
Attorney and Executive
Secretary

Louis J. Woolf
Executive Committee

Frank W. Green
Executive Committee

Don C. Jenks
Executive Committee

E. N. Heinz
Executive Committee

in 1942 when Congress passed an amendment to the Revenue Act. "Our entire efforts during the aforesaid period of time have culminated in the passage of the drawback proviso," reported Hall. "As passed by Congress, (it) was a compromise measure and not in conformity with our recommendations." Nevertheless, the amendment established a tax differential in the form of a drawback that offered some relief to manufacturers and, indirectly, to consumers. For example, in November 1942, a $6 per proof gallon tax was allowed a drawback of $3.75, bringing the net tax back down to $2.25 per proof gallon.

FEMA's Research Committee was also active during the decade, beginning work on defining vanilla extract in 1942. By 1946, the committee had started to compile data on vanilla extracts. Pending the adoption of a federal standard, FEMA issued reports to its members about its research as well as legal developments. One such advisory contained the following information:

- All words in the name "Imitation vanilla flavor" should be displayed with equal prominence. It is not regarded as essential that the word "flavor" follow the words "imitation vanilla."
- At least 13.35 ounces of vanilla beans should be employed in the manufacture of each gallon of vanilla extract.
- It has been established in the laboratories of the Food and Drug Administration that vanilla extract made from vanilla oleoresin varies in flavor, odor

and chemical composition from vanilla extract made directly from the beans, as provided in the advisory definition and standard for vanilla extract. Therefore, vanilla extract made from vanilla oleoresin should be labeled to indicate that fact.

As the world slid deeper into war, the industry experienced many problems with government allocations of materials and delays in importation of raw materials. German U-boats added to the difficulties by wreaking havoc in shipping lanes. "To the importers of essential oils, as well as of every other foreign article, this menace continues to be one of the most serious problems we have to face," Francis T. Dodge of Dodge & Olcott Co. reported to FEMA's annual meeting in 1943.

In the same report, Dodge pointed out that prices for raw materials such as lemon, orange, and lime oil and vanilla beans had risen dramatically since the war began, nearly doubling in some cases. Price wasn't the only obstacle. "In many instances, where American importers are ready and anxious to bring in essential oils from abroad, and where the sellers are anxious to ship, the greatest difficulty is experienced in obtaining the necessary freight space," he added.

Glycerin, another important ingredient in the industry, was also tightly controlled during the war years. "You are hereby requested to ship no glycerin to anyone except on a sworn statement that immediate shipments are essential for direct defense requirements

continued on page 75

71

1940

Flour is first fortified with vitamins and iron.

1941

Japanese attack Pearl Harbor.

1944

Esmond Snell and Herschel Mitchell discover folic acid, a B vitamin needed to make DNA and RNA.

The University of California, Davis, creates a Division of Food Technology.

1945

Frozen orange juice developed for the war effort is made commercially under the Snow Crop brand, which later became Minute Maid.

World War II ends with the formal Japanese surrender on Sept. 2.

The first computer, the Electronic Numerical Integrator And Computer (ENIAC), is completed at the Moore School of Engineering at the University of Pennsylvania in Philadelphia. The ENIAC weighs more than 60,000 pounds and has more than 18,000 vacuum tubes.

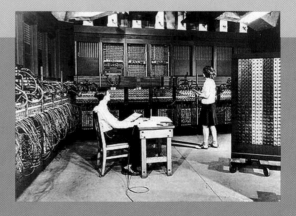

1945

The microwave oven is invented by
Dr. Percy Spencer at the Raytheon Company.

Edward M. Purcell first observes nuclear magnetic resonance
(NMR) in an after-hours experiment while completing work
on the classic 27-volume series of books on radar. Though
initially used in physics, NMR has been applied powerfully
as an analytic method for elucidating chemical structure and
materials properties.

1948

Alexander Schonberg et al. complete the first comprehensive study of the
reaction of a-amino acids. Schonberg coins the phrase "Strecker degradation"
to describe reactions of amino acids with carbonyl containing compounds.

William McKinley Martin introduces the Dole aseptic process:
high-temperature, short-time sterilization of a food and its container
independently, filling of the container with the product in a sterile
atmosphere, and sealing of the lid.

The Moon is Down...

THERE are dark nights in Norway. Nights when Nazi sentries feel uneasy at their posts.

It is not what they hear that disturbs them. It is what they do *not* hear. The deep silence behind a bush. The stealthy quiet around the corner of a house. The terrible hush in the blackness all around them.

For the Norwegians lost their country without ever surrendering themselves. They wait now in the night to strike back at their oppressors.

If they ever *had* really given in, there would be no need of the thousands of Nazi troops now in Norway. They could have been sent to the Russian front. Or Tunisia. *But they couldn't be spared.*

They can't be spared in Holland either. Or Poland or France or Yugoslavia or Belgium. In China, tens of thousands of Jap troops must also remain. And Axis troops will have to remain in countless countries so long as the "conquered" people have the stamina to resist.

You can help support *this army already in Europe*—by your contribution to the National War Fund, which you make through the New York Committee.

For this year, the agencies that can do this job have banded together to make the collection and distribution of funds simpler, cheaper and more effective. Their job is two-fold. To keep our fighting allies in the fight. To provide friendly help for our men in the armed services.

Because all these agencies are now banded together, you are being asked to contribute only *once for all* of them. Because you are being asked to give only once, you are also being asked to give *generously*. Add up all you would have given to each of these agencies throughout the year, and then *double the total!* It is one of the most important contributions you can make to victory!

Give
ONCE
for
ALL
26

NATIONAL AGENCIES

USO
United Seamen's Service
War Prisoners Aid
Belgian War Relief Society
British War Relief Society
French Relief Fund
Friends of Luxembourg
Greek War Relief Association
Norwegian Relief

Polish War Relief
Queen Wilhelmina Fund
Russian War Relief
United China Relief
United Czechoslovak Relief
United Yugoslav Relief Fund
Refugees Relief Trustees
United States Committee for the
Care of European Children

NEW YORK AGENCIES

New York City Defense
Recreation Committee
American Women's Voluntary
Services
C.D.V.O.-Community

English Speaking Union
New York City Women's
Council of the Navy

WINE & LIQUOR DIVISION

NATIONAL
WAR FUND

LEWIS S. ROSENSTIEL
Chairman

SPACE CONTRIBUTED BY

THE WINE REVIEW

If this Card is found it must be returned at once to the Deputy Director of Rationing, Brisbane.

Commonwealth of Australia

QK 96445

1943
MEAT
RATION CARD
Rg. D.1

Issued to
Name

Address

NEVER BUY RATIONED GOODS
WITHOUT RATION STAMPS
NEVER PAY MORE THAN THE LEGAL PRICE

United States Office of Price Administration

IMPORTANT: When you have used your ration, salvage the TIN CANS and WASTE FATS. They are needed to make munitions for our fighting men. Cooperate with your local Salvage Committee.

☆ U. S. GOVERNMENT PRINTING OFFICE : 1943   16—35570-1

Ungerer & Company's plant in Totowa, N.J., circa 1947

continued from page 71

or medical and pharmaceutical uses, or that such shipments are essential to prevent shutdown of plants," Roscoe C. Edlund, manager of the Association of American Soap and Glycerine Producers, reported to FEMA in 1942. The same held true for spices; a government conservation order issued in 1942 limited the amount of seasonings manufacturers could buy, except for orders being delivered to government agencies such as the army and navy.

Some of the wartime restrictions carried on even after the fighting stopped in 1945. In 1946, Hoyt Bonner, vice president of Lamborn & Co. in New York City, reported on the rationing of sugar as well as government controls on essential oils and vanillin. Bonner stated, ". . . The controls which now exist and which have been in force since December 1941 have a stranglehold on every phase of sugar and could not be more

THE SATURDAY EVENING POST

Now You'll *Like* Yeast!

1 *Mash a cake of Fleischmann's Yeast in dry glass with a fork*

2 *Add 1/4 glass cool, plain tomato juice . . . or milk . . . or water*

3 *Stir till yeast is completely blended*

4 *Fill glass with liquid . . . stir and drink*

If you are one of the millions who know what Fleischmann's Yeast can do for you, but never stayed with it long enough to get its full benefit, you'll now find it easy to take this new pleasant way. Remember, for daily use, Fleischmann's Yeast is one of the richest of all common foods in the amazing vitamin B complex. Drink it last thing at night . . . first thing in the morning.

Fleischmann's *Fresh* Yeast

DRINK IT . . . TO YOUR HEALTH!

AMERICA'S FAVORITE
PEANUT SPREAD

Full of Delicious, Chewey
Bits of Fresh Roasted Peanuts

HOLSUM PRODUCTS
Milwaukee, Wis.   Kansas City, Mo.

complete." The situation was just as serious for vanillin. "There just doesn't seem to be any available at this time," Bonner said. "I venture to say that if the [price] ceiling was taken off vanillin, we would have a great deal more production . . ."

Sugar also continued to play a role in the

economics of the industry long after the war's end. The market for sugar was in steady decline during 1947-48 because of the top-heavy supply situation and household and industrial hoarding sprees. "Since January 19, 1948, the price for a hundred pound bag of standard cane refiners' sugar has dropped in the New England, Middle Atlantic and Pacific Coast states ninety points, from $8.40 to $7.50, and in the balance of the country a full one hundred points . . ." according to a report issued in 1948. "Even with these declines, the price structure is still

PLANT A VICTORY GARDEN

OUR FOOD IS FIGHTING

A GARDEN WILL MAKE YOUR RATIONS GO FURTHER

in a somewhat shaky condition."

As FEMA's sphere of activities on behalf of its members had grown over the years, so too had its budget. Its total receipts on June 1, 1940, for example, topped $10,500--more than enough to balance its expenditures, including railway fares ($1,144.50),

stenography ($469.95), telephone and telegraph ($124.51), and dues to belong to the U.S. Chamber of Commerce ($10). That same year, FEMA held its largest annual meeting to date in Chicago, Ill., at the Drake Hotel.

At the close of the decade, FEMA celebrated its 40th anniversary. As FEMA President John N. Curlett

of McCormick & Company noted, the goodwill FEMA had engendered over the years was one of its greatest assets: "Goodwill has very little cash value, but without it an association is poor indeed." Willoughby McCormick and the other founding members had a vision, but as Curlett pointed out, "little did they dream that this association would carry on for a period of 40 years or more to strive for better business relations, improved conditions in the industry, advancement of the ideals in which they believed, and serve as a model for other groups."

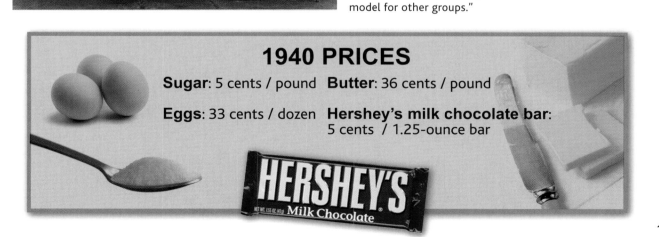

1940 PRICES

Sugar: 5 cents / pound   **Butter**: 36 cents / pound

Eggs: 33 cents / dozen   **Hershey's milk chocolate bar**: 5 cents / 1.25-ounce bar

Chapter 6
1950~1959

*M*arked by continuing post-World War II optimism and the United States' emergence as a superpower on the world scene, the 1950s were heady years for many Americans. Despite the nuclear arms race, a new, more prosperous way of life seemed possible thanks to a stable economy, booming demand for consumer goods, and technological achievements like the first transcontinental television broadcast and the first polio vaccine. As scientists were able to direct and accelerate their efforts toward peaceful activities rather than meeting wartime needs, the decade became a turning point for both FEMA and the flavor industry.

FEMA began the decade with its 41st annual convention at the Hotel Traymore in Atlantic City, N.J., where FEMA President John N. Curlett of McCormick & Company noted, "Organizations such as ours are, in many ways, the natural result of one effort to explore the constant changes

Photo courtesy of Pope Lime Company Inc., www.popelime.com

The FEMA Golden Anniversary Banquet at the Hotel Roosevelt in New York City during the 1959 annual meeting

FEMA tracked members' dues on file cards

which characterize the complex world of today."

Change was indeed constant. The food industry and food ingredient manufacturers saw a significant proliferation of federal laws, and the states continued to introduce their own laws related to the food industry. At the 1951 convention, FEMA reported that nearly 1,700 bills directly involving the industry had been introduced in Congress and various state legislatures during the most recent legislative period. As in previous decades, the majority of activity occurred in California (114 bills) and New York (109 bills), but almost every state passed new legislation that could affect the flavor industry.

While some states enacted revised food, drug and cosmetic acts patterned after federal legislation, many of the bills introduced in state legislatures aimed to increase sales and use taxes, state income taxes, and licensing and registration fees to maintain various state commissions, boards and agencies. All of these laws led to regulations that the association needed to report on to members. Sometimes, the new regulations also created problems for the flavor industry.

As in earlier decades, the industry and FEMA continued to work on establishing standards for vanilla

and other extracts. "Since 1946 the Research Committee has been actively engaged in compiling data on vanilla extracts, much of which is pertinent to the subject of 'standards' for this flavor," Dr. K.R. Newman, chairman of the Scientific Research Committee, told the 1953 FEMA annual meeting. "During the current year additional data have been compiled that likewise are a

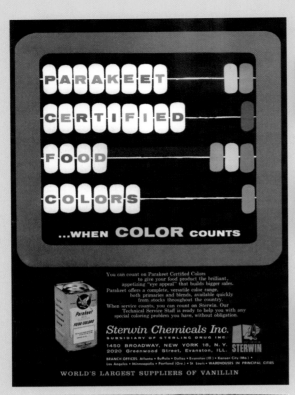
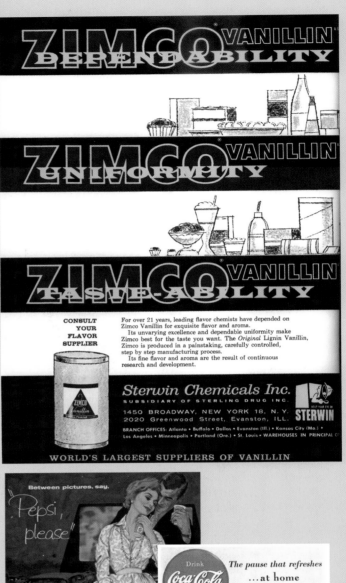

Don Gussow
Publisher & Editor
Ronald M. Foster, Jr.
Managing Editor
Dan Burns
Associate Editor
John B. Mulligan
Advertising Manager

Candy Industry

NEWS OF CONFECTIONERY MANUFACTURING AND MARKETING

220 East 42nd Street   Murray Hill 7-8771   New York 17, N. Y.

May 29, 1953

Mr. John S. Hall, Executive Secretary
Flavoring Extract Manufacturers' Association
of the United States
1051 First National Bank Building
Chicago 3, Illinois

Dear John:

Enclosed is an extra print of the photograph
which you may want for your files.

Kindest regards.

Sincerely,

DG:sf
encl.

PUBLISHED EVERY OTHER TUESDAY BY DON GUSSOW PUBLICATIONS, INC., ALSO PUBLISHERS OF
"THE CANDY INDUSTRY CATALOG AND FORMULA BOOK," "BOTTLING INDUSTRY" AND "FROZEN FOOD AGE"

Executive Secretary John S. Hall at the 1953 FEMA annual meeting

contribution to the general fund of knowledge related to vanilla extracts."

Some extract manufacturers feared they would lose sales if new standards lessened the value of their use of the term "vanilla." There was also a great deal of ignorance about vanilla beans and the flavor they produced. "The extract industry should face the fact that vanilla is the least known, most restricted flavor in the U.S. food economy today," Ray C. Schlotterer, secretary of the Vanilla Bean Association, reported to FEMA at its 1957 annual meeting. "A greater opportunity lies ahead to reintroduce Vanilla — not just as a romantic, cherished name but as a meaningful, important element of flavor and nutrition that every consumer can expect to enjoy when he sees the label — Vanilla flavored."

To help maintain the integrity of pure vanilla extract, FEMA began conducting research at the Boyce-Thompson Institute for Plant Research in New York to establish basic knowledge that could be used to detect adulteration of vanilla extracts. This research became a major focus of FEMA for a significant part of the half century to follow. "The aim of the research ... is to study the constitution of authentic vanilla extracts, and isolate and characterize components in pure vanilla products that can be used as a basis for enforceable legal standards of identity," Dr. Arthur S. Wendt, chairman of the Scientific Research Committee, reported at the 1956 annual meeting. "... The problem is by no means simple. If it were, governmental agencies would have solved it long ago."

By the end of the decade, FEMA researchers were beginning to use the recently developed analytical methods of gas chromatography on vanilla extracts. Although its potential had not been completely explored, the new technology seemed as versatile as traditional paper chromatography, even though the results obtained on authentic vanilla extracts were not

continued on page 87

83

1950

Korean War begins.

1952

A.T. James and Archer J.P. Martin's presentation on gas chromatography at the Society for Analytical Chemistry meeting in Oxford, England, draws immediate attention from the audience of industrial analysts. This technique for separating volatiles revolutionizes the study of flavor compounds.

1953

John Hodge publishes his classic paper on the chemistry of browning reactions in model systems, summarizing the basic amino carbonyl interactions in the Maillard reaction and the subsequent reaction routes.

1953

U.S. Army begins food irradiation program.

James Watson, Francis Crick and Maurice Wilkins discover the double-helix structure of DNA, laying the foundation for understanding genetics and developing recombinant DNA technology.

Korean War ends with signing of armistice on July 27.

1954

The Society of Flavor Chemists is founded in New York City.

1954

FDA bans coumarin, a constituent of some commercial vanilla preparations.

New pasteurization process invented to aseptically pack pure chilled juice in glass bottles, allowing it to be shipped and stored without refrigeration.

1957

European Economic Community is established.

1958

The Food Additives Amendment to the 1938 Food, Drug, and Cosmetic Act is enacted, creating the GRAS provision.

1959

FEMA

FEMA takes its first steps to establish the FEMA GRAS Program.

Board of Governors of F.E.M.A. for 1959-60

E. N. Heinz, Jr.
President

Charles P. McCormick, Jr.
1st Vice-President

S. M. Kleinschmidt
2nd Vice-President

Dr. A. S. Wendt
3rd Vice-President

Hunt P. Wilson
Secretary

Lloyd E. Smith
Treasurer

John S. Hall
Attorney and Executive
Secretary

Don C. Jenks

Robert Krone

Francis C. Oakley

J. R. Leitz

Robert H. Pulver

Dr. J. H. McGlumphy

continued from page 83

nearly as uniform. The 1950s saw only the beginning use of this technology, but the learning curve in later years would have a great impact on the flavor industry. (See page 156, "The Development of Instrumental Methods of Analysis and Their Impact on the Flavor Industry.")

Training flavor scientists was one of the key roles played by FEMA during the decade, and the association often worked hand in hand with educational institutions. "The greater the knowledge and experience with food manufacture each of you has, the better you will be able to assist your prospective customers in the proper use of flavors and to prevent failures in new food product development," Dr. Ernest Lockhart, with the Department of Food Technology of the Massachusetts Institute of Technology, said at FEMA's 1953 annual meeting. "The

best way for you to overcome obstacles ... is to have among your personnel men who know food manufacture and the effects of food processing in its many forms on flavor quality. Food technologists, such as we develop ... have a training that fits these difficult requirements as closely as is possible within the limits imposed by sound educational philosophy."

In addition to working with educational institutions, FEMA's good relationship with the Food and Drug Administration served the association well during the 1950s, as it had in previous decades. Before Dr. J.W. Sale retired from the FDA in 1953, he spoke to the annual FEMA meeting that year about the importance of the "constructive cooperation" between the food industry and the federal government — and

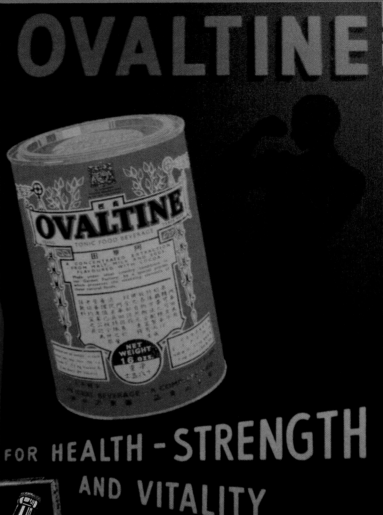

FEMA warmly reciprocated. "We have always received very fine cooperation when we have gone to Washington to call on Dr. Sale," said FEMA Secretary L.P. Symmes. "He has always given us a fair and impartial hearing. Our association has always had the benefit of his advice and counsel in solving problems that have arisen from time to time. In other words, he has been sort of a friendly godfather to us on many, many important occasions."

Other Washington stalwarts also welcomed FEMA's representation. In 1956 FEMA was recognized by the U.S.

Chamber of Commerce as one of its charter members
that had maintained its membership continuously.
The association was featured in a special publication
issued at the chamber's 44th annual meeting that
year. "Our Association has deemed it a privilege to
participate in a National Federation dedicated to good
government, good citizenship, and good business, which
the Chamber has fostered since its inception," FEMA
replied in accepting the prestigious citation.

Reflecting the growing sophistication of science

and technology as the decade progressed, FEMA's members turned their attention to the age-old question of what constitutes zero risk and exposure, as illustrated in a report by the Research Committee in 1957. The committee concluded that the term "practical equivalent of zero" had no rigorous scientific basis, and that to designate a finite concentration as zero could not be justified scientifically — although it might be legally expedient to do so. The committee's report also stated that a "harmless" or "trivial" level of any substance in foods could only be determined on the basis of a quantitative study of its biological effects or, in other words, by the establishment of a tolerated level. "The committee has in mind ... a mathematical or statistical derivation rather than the present rule-of-thumb factor of safety," according to the report.

During the late 1950s, concerns arose about the flavoring substance safrole, a constituent of oil of sassafras.

Where you work

*The pause that refreshes
with ice-cold Coca-Cola*

Photo courtesy of Pope Lime Company Inc., www.popelime.com

Remembering the sudden withdrawal of coumarin from the market several years earlier after a long history of apparently safe use, FEMA's Board of Governors decided to take constructive action. The board hired Dr. Bernard Oser of Food and Drug Research Laboratories to serve as FEMA's first consulting scientific director. Oser would also later become the founder and first chairman of the FEMA Expert Panel. (See Chapter 7.) One of Oser's first tasks was to meet with the FDA and review the agency's data on safrole. "It is imperative to continue close cooperation with the FDA, through Dr. Oser and our Food Additive Committee, not only to get the facts governing the safe use of safrole, but to avoid surprise in any future moves in the situation," the association reported in 1958.

That same year, the Food Additives Amendment was enacted, and the safety of food additives became a major focus of the flavor and food industries. As the 1950s ended, FEMA was poised to launch a program that would become a scientific landmark for evaluating food additive safety — the FEMA GRAS Program and the FEMA Expert Panel. The next decade would usher in the Space Age and a new wave of technological innovation — and FEMA would be ready.

1950 PRICES

Sugar: 10 cents / pound **Butter:** 73 cents / pound

Eggs: 60 cents / dozen **Hershey's milk chocolate bar:** 5 cents / 1-ounce bar

HERSHEY'S Milk Chocolate

Chapter 7
1960-1969

*M*ost Americans think of the 1960s as a time of unrest — dissatisfaction with an increasingly unpopular war in Vietnam, the assassinations of President John F. Kennedy, Martin Luther King Jr., and Robert Kennedy, the tragedy of Kent State, and the riots at the Democratic National Convention. For FEMA, it was a time of decisions that would determine the role and policies of the association for the rest of the century and beyond.

In groundbreaking actions in 1960, the Food and Drug Administration banned safrole from use in foods based on a finding of carcinogenicity, and Congress passed the Color Additive Amendment, which — like the Food Additives Amendment of 1958 — included a Delaney Clause prohibiting the addition of carcinogenic color additives to food. Thus, for colors as well as for food additives, these new pieces of legislation abandoned the outdated concept of "poisonous per se," and replaced it with the recognition that there could be conditions of use that posed no practical risk of harm.

The 1958 passage of the Food Additives Amendment to the Food, Drug, and Cosmetic Act had already set the stage for FEMA's activities in the early 1960s. The FDA needed data, and FEMA provided it. In the first few months of 1960, two of FEMA's committees, the Food Additives Committee (FAC) and the Scientific Research Committee (SRC), tabulated and summarized the results of a large, complex survey of more than 1,000 natural and artificial flavoring ingredients then in use. Responses were received from more than 100 flavor and food companies. The entire task was performed manually by volunteers from FEMA member companies; at that time there were no appropriate computer facilities available. The collated results were summarized in writing on keysort cards, an early and altogether too cumbersome

attempt at manual punch card technology. A set of the cards was provided to the FDA.

Early in 1960 the FDA had published a final list of natural flavors it considered to be "generally recognized as safe" (GRAS), omitting some that had been on a list FEMA had proposed. The agency also published a very short list of 27 single chemical entities, such as vanillin, that it also considered GRAS. In a series of conversations and conferences with FEMA representatives in the first few months of the year, the agency expressed doubt that it could consider many more flavoring ingredients to be GRAS. As one possible solution, it proposed that FEMA file food additive petitions for the remainder.

FEMA and its scientific director, Dr. Bernard Oser, did not believe it possible or appropriate for the association to meet the requirement of compiling food additive petitions for flavoring substances for two reasons: the very large number of substances then in use, and the fact that the available scientific information did not support the need for such a detailed safety review.

FEMA concluded that the food additive petition route would not work for FDA or the flavor industry and would not provide any significant benefit to consumers. Oser and the chair of the FAC, Dr. Richard Hall of McCormick & Company, recommended that FEMA pursue an independent course explicitly provided for by Congress.

The Food Additives Amendment included new Section 201(s) of the Federal Food, Drug, and Cosmetic Act, which provided that a substance could be judged to be "generally recognized as safe" (GRAS) by "experts qualified by training and experience to judge its safety" and not be subject to the requirements for a food additive petition.

In one of the most significant actions in its history, FEMA established a panel of acknowledged experts, independent of the industry, to evaluate the information on flavoring ingredients and decide which were GRAS. The panel held its first meeting in October 1960. (See page 102 for more information on FEMA GRAS.)

At the annual meeting of the Institute of Food Technologists in 1961, L.M. Beacham Jr. of the FDA commented that the FDA would not "challenge" FEMA GRAS due to the agency's confidence in the FEMA program. Later that year, FEMA's FAC reported that a partial list of GRAS substances would be published. In 1962, the panel began to review some botanically derived natural flavors, and plans for toxicity testing required by the panel began to move forward.

Since the mid-'50s, and particularly since the passage of the Food Additives Amendment, it had become obvious that "safe use" of food additives would require specifications of purity. In 1962, the National Academy of Sciences began work on a Food Chemicals Codex (FCC). A FEMA committee with Tony Filandro of Virginia Dare Extract Co., Inc. as chair began to address flavoring ingredients specifications and contributed its work to the FCC. In 1966, Part 1 of the FCC appeared; flavors later grew to be the largest category of food ingredient in this compendium. The new instrumental methods of analysis, especially gas chromatography (see page 156), became especially important in determining specifications for flavoring ingredients.

During the early '60s, the FDA, while recognizing the validity of FEMA's lengthening GRAS list, had begun to be uncomfortable about having no official position on FEMA GRAS substances. This was particularly true when responding to inquiries from other governments. By 1964, FEMA's FAC had begun working closely with the FDA on a comprehensive publication of GRAS substances. The FDA called upon the assistance of the Department of Agriculture to help assure that the natural sources of flavoring ingredients were properly identified by their botanical names.

Mid-decade, FEMA faced some organizational changes. In 1964, John Hall, the attorney and executive secretary of FEMA, died after serving the association loyally for many years. Daniel R. Thompson of Washington, D.C., who brought a fresh perspective to the post, succeeded him.

In February 1965, two key items appeared in *Food Technology*: "GRAS 3," the first publication of a comprehensive list of substances judged to be GRAS by the Expert Panel, and the "White List" of FDA-approved natural flavors. In a further demonstration of confidence in the FEMA GRAS program, the FDA included nearly all FEMA GRAS substances in a food additives regulation, except those in ongoing toxicity studies. The FDA also distributed copies of GRAS 3 to all its regional offices. Art Schramm of Allied Chemicals became chair of the FAC, and FEMA,

the Expert Panel, and FEMA's scientific director, Oser, began to consider what course of action to follow with new flavoring substances in the future.

In response to the growing list of global issues in the industry, FEMA representatives met with a number of European flavor producers in 1967 and took the first steps toward formation of the International Organization of the Flavor Industry (IOFI). Also in 1967, the Joint FAO/WHO Expert Committee on Food Additives (JECFA) for the first time addressed the subject of flavoring ingredients. Members at that meeting were Oser and Hall from the United States, and Dr. C. A. Vodoz from Switzerland. Both then and for years afterward, FEMA was nearly the only source of reliable data on flavoring ingredient safety and use. From the flavor industry's point of view, this initial meeting was not helpful; the committee for the most part tended to apply to flavors the same routine approach to testing and evaluation they would apply to pesticide residues. It would be nearly 30 years before a better approach was adopted by JECFA.

In 1968, FEMA's FAC, with Dr. Jack Krum of Sterwin Chemicals as chair, began planning for an update of the 1959-60 flavoring ingredients survey. Prompted in part by the FDA, FEMA decided it should explore all feasible routes toward approval of new flavoring ingredients. After a thorough evaluation, FEMA decided on one route: the GRAS evaluation through the Expert Panel.

In 1969 Dr. Richard Ford joined FEMA's staff as a consultant and took over maintenance of the flavoring ingredients files, support of the Expert Panel, and much of the planning for the forthcoming survey.

FEMA's Scientific Research Committee, under Drs. Arthur Wendt of Fred Fear and Company and David Jorysch of H. Kohnstamm, continued work on the development of newer, far more sensitive and discriminating methods of detecting the adulteration of vanilla extract that had begun in the previous decade. First efforts used paper chromatography to discover foreign botanicals and analyze vanilla organic acids; later efforts increasingly used gas chromatography, especially for the volatile components (see page 156). By 1965, it seemed that the work on effective methods of detecting vanilla adulteration might have been drawing to a successful close, but of course that never happened. The battle between ever more subtle adulteration and ever more sensitive methods of detecting continues today. At the same time, concern over vanilla was joined by concern over the adulteration of fruit flavors and extracts.

The need for a federal standard of identity for vanilla flavors had long been a matter of discussion within the association, but had been held in abeyance by the obvious lack of any effective methods of enforcing one. Furthermore, there was disagreement on whether any such standard should be based on the traditional requirement of a "unit weight of vanilla beans" being 13.35 ounces of vanilla beans, regardless of moisture content, or instead should be based on 10 ounces dry weight of beans — equivalent to 13.35 ounces of beans

continued on page 100

The 2009 FEMA Expert Panel

Samuel M. Cohen, M.D., Ph.D. - University of Nebraska Medical Center

Nigel J. Gooderham, Ph.D. - Imperial College School of Medicine, University of London

Lawrence J. Marnett, Ph.D. - Vanderbilt University School of Medicine

Philip S. Portoghese, Ph.D. - University of Minnesota

Ivonne M.C.M. Rietjens, Ph.D. - Wageningen University (Netherlands)

Robert L. Smith, Ph.D., D.Sc. - Imperial College School of Medicine, University of London

William J. Waddell, M.D., Ph.D. - University of Louisville School of Medicine

1960

First commercial plant for freeze-drying food opens, and freeze-dried coffee enters the marketplace.

Safrole, a key ingredient in root beer, is banned, and manufacturers and flavor companies scramble to reformulate. Solution: methyl salicylate with other items such as methyl chavicol and anethole.

Theodore Maiman, an employee of Hughes Aircraft Co., develops the first working laser.

1961

The first aseptic filling plant for milk opens in Switzerland.

1962

W.H. McFadden and Roy Teranishi couple a gas chromatograph to a time-of-flight (TOF) mass spectrometer and apply this technique to aroma research. This early GC-TOF system has a major disadvantage: Sensitivity is poor due to the high split ratio required to maintain the vacuum in the mass spectrometer. The invention of gas separators that can efficiently remove the GC carrier gas prior to introduction into the mass spectrometer opens the door to the analysis and identification of complex mixtures.

First publications appear on methyl jasmonate and methyl dihydrojasmonate.

1963

First commercial liquid chromatograph is introduced by Jim Waters, founder and leader of Waters Associates.

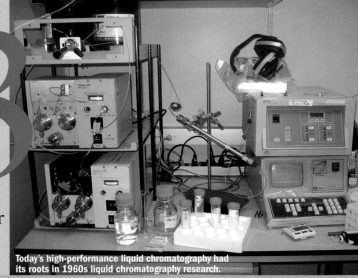

Today's high-performance liquid chromatography had its roots in 1960s liquid chromatography research.

FDA approves irradiation to disinfest wheat and wheat flour.

1964

FDA approves irradiation to inhibit sprouting in potatoes.

1965

First publications appear on isolation of Furaneol® from strawberry and pineapple.

1967

Texas Instruments creates the first handheld calculator.

South African surgeon Christiaan Barnard conducts the first heart transplant on 53-year-old Lewis Washkansky.

1968

Computer system is developed to automatically record mass spectra, allowing continuous scanning and recording of mass spectra at 4-second intervals.

IOFI 1969

The International Organization of the Flavor Industry (IOFI) is founded.

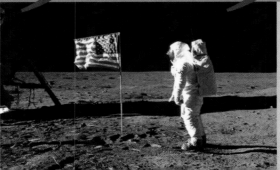

Neil Armstrong becomes the first man to walk on the moon.

99

continued from page 95

containing 25 percent moisture. The existence of new, more accurate analytical methods led to the filing of a Citizen's Petition with the FDA in 1960 for a standard based on 10 ounces of beans, dry weight by a leading manufacturer of vanilla extract. Other companies filed for a standard based on 13.35 ounces, wet weight. The FDA resolved the matter in 1963 through a compromise that established a definition of "unit weight of vanilla beans" as 13.35 ounces of beans containing "not more than 25 percent moisture, and, in the case of vanilla beans containing more than 25 percent moisture, it means the weight of such beans equivalent in content of moisture free vanilla-bean solids to 13.35 ounces of vanilla beans containing 25 percent moisture."

After years of hearings and negotiations, in 1964 the FDA published proposed standards of intense interest

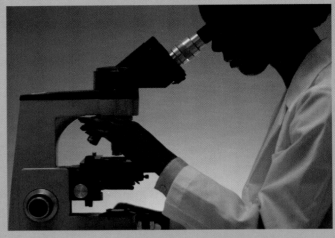

to FEMA: for frozen desserts, including vanilla ice cream, and for noncarbonated and fruit-based beverages.

Another major FEMA initiative was the joint government/FEMA/private sector vanilla agronomy program. Begun in the 1950s at the Federal Experiment

FEMA GRAS Publications

GRAS PUBLICATION	FEMA NUMBERS	Number of Reviewed Substances	REFERENCE
3	2001-3124	1,124	Hall and Oser, 1965
4	3125-3249	125	Hall and Oser, 1970
5	3250-3325	76	Oser and Hall, 1972
6	3326-3390	65	Oser and Ford, 1973a
7	3391-3423	33	Oser and Ford, 1973b
8	3424-3444	21	Oser and Ford, 1974
9	3445-3476	32	Oser and Ford, 1975
10	3477-3525	49	Oser and Ford, 1977
11	3526-3596	71	Oser and Ford, 1978
12	3597-3650	54	Oser and Ford, 1979
13	3651-3739	89	Oser et al., 1984
14	3740-3754	15	Oser et al., 1985
15	3755-3774	20	Burdock et al., 1990
16	3775-3796	22	Smith and Ford, 1993
17	3797-3815	19	Smith et al., 1996
18	3816-3905	90	Newberne et al., 1998
19	3906-3963	58	Newberne et al., 2000
20	3964-4023	60	Smith et al., 2001
21	4024-4068	45	Smith et al., 2003
22	4069-4253	185	Smith et al., 2005
23	4254-4429	176	Waddell et al., 2007
24	4430-4666	237	Smith et al., 2009

NOTE: The "GRAS 1" and "GRAS 2" publications were background reports in *Food Technology* explaining the bases for the FEMA GRAS program and did not contain any lists of GRAS flavoring substances.

Station in Mayaguez, Puerto Rico, its objective was to improve the cultivation and productivity of vanilla. In 1968, researchers at the Experiment Station began to encounter difficulties because of root rot in the field plantings, and this program was never quite able to live up to its promise of developing a reliable source of vanilla outside of Madagascar. The mid-'60s saw many meetings, sometimes useful, sometimes frustrating, between FEMA representatives and the government of Madagascar over the pricing and supply of vanilla beans and efforts to promote greater use of pure vanilla by consumers.

In 1968, concern over the safety of the artificial sweetener cyclamate and the flavor enhancer monosodium glutamate (MSG) prompted President Richard Nixon to order a review of the safety of all GRAS food ingredients, including flavors. Ironically, in retrospect, neither cyclamate nor MSG posed significant risks, but the consequences remain with us today.

FEMA entered the 1960s as an effective but not widely known trade association. When the decade ended, FEMA was known both nationally and internationally as the recognized source of information on the safety of flavors.

FEMA Scientific Directors

Dr. Ben Oser 1960-1969
Dr. Richard Hall 1969-1974
Dr. Richard Ford 1974-1981

Dr. Bruce Bernard 1981-1985
Dr. George Burdock 1985-1992

John Hallagan 1992-2001
Dr. Tim Adams 2001-Present

1960 PRICES

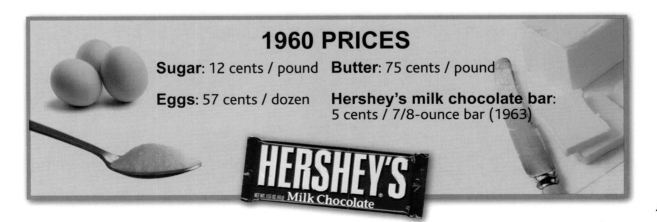

Sugar: 12 cents / pound **Butter**: 75 cents / pound

Eggs: 57 cents / dozen **Hershey's milk chocolate bar**: 5 cents / 7/8-ounce bar (1963)

The FEMA GRAS program – FEMA's crown jewel

By J. B. Hallagan, T. B. Adams and R. L. Hall

In 1959, under the leadership of Drs. Ben Oser and Richard Hall, FEMA began a novel program to assess the safety and GRAS (generally recognized as safe) status of flavor ingredients under the authority provided by the new 1958 Food Additives Amendment to the Food, Drug, and Cosmetic Act, the federal law governing the regulation of flavors and other food ingredients. Since then, the FEMA GRAS program has become the longest-running and most widely recognized and admired industry GRAS assessment program.

The FEMA program began in 1959 with a survey of the flavor industry to identify flavor ingredients then in use and to provide estimates of the amounts of these substances used to manufacture flavors. Oser, FEMA's first scientific director, organized the initial Expert Panel in 1960, beginning the panel's evaluation of flavor ingredient safety that continues today. Then and now,

the Expert Panel usually consists of six to eight members and has comprised some of the world's top experts in toxicology, pathology and biochemistry.

The Expert Panel's GRAS assessments have applied a number of modern techniques of safety evaluation, including the use of metabolic studies and structural relationships that had not previously been applied in a significant manner to food ingredients such as flavoring substances. While the Expert Panel has been provided with financial support by FEMA, the panel has always maintained total independence in its operations and GRAS determinations.

Beginning with the Expert Panel's first publication in 1965 ("GRAS 3"), more than 2,300 single chemically defined flavoring substances and about 300 natural flavor complexes have been determined by the panel to be "FEMA GRAS." The Expert Panel has published 22 reports announcing the GRAS status of new flavoring substances in the journal *Food Technology*. (See box on page 100 for details.) The Expert Panel has regularly published its criteria for its GRAS determinations.

In addition to the GRAS publications, the Expert Panel and the FEMA scientific staff have published more than 50 original reports and reviews in peer-reviewed scientific literature, ranging from reports on the safety of individual flavoring substances to extensive reviews ("group summaries") on groups of structurally related flavoring substances. FEMA staff and consultants have also published a number of reports explaining the scientific and legal bases for the FEMA program.

A key aspect of the FEMA program's success is the fact that all information used by the Expert Panel in its GRAS assessments is shared with the chief regulator of the U.S. flavor industry, the Food and Drug Administration,

The first FEMA Expert Panel with FEMA's Dr. Richard L. Hall (center), photographed by FEXPAN Chairman Dr. Bernard L. Oser. From left: Drs. David W. Fassett, Maurice H. Seevers, Horace W. Gerarde, Hall, Lauren A. Woods, Jacob Stekol and Horace C. Spencer

so that the agency may make its own judgments on the validity of the Expert Panel's GRAS decisions. Information from the Expert Panel's GRAS assessments is entered into FDA's database and also into the flavor industry's database maintained jointly with the fragrance industry through the Research Institute for Fragrance Materials (RIFM). The FEMA/RIFM database is available to all FEMA members and is an invaluable source of information for flavor manufacturers as they develop new flavoring substances and comply with various national and global regulatory requirements.

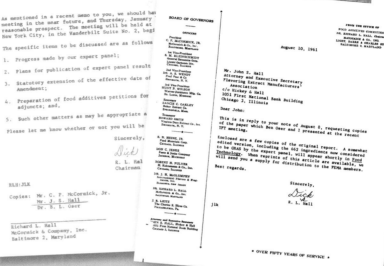

The years since 1995, a period of increasing globalization in business and regulation, have represented an extremely active period for the FEMA GRAS program. During this time, the size of the FEMA GRAS list has nearly doubled. Also during this time, the FEMA Expert Panel thoroughly reviewed and revised their criteria for determining GRAS status for single chemically defined flavor ingredients and natural flavor complexes. They published in the peer-reviewed scientific literature detailed reviews of structurally related groups of flavoring substances. In addition, the Expert Panel published a number of reports resolving issues associated with the safety and FEMA GRAS status of numerous individual flavoring substances.

Over the years the Expert Panel continued and carefully expanded its use of structure/activity relationships in the evaluation of the safety in use of flavoring ingredients. Drawing on and extending that experience, in 1978 Greg Cramer, Dr. Richard Ford and Dr. Hall published a "Decision Tree" paper that provided for the first time an organized approach to the use of structure/activity relationships in the evaluation of safety. The Decision Tree classifies substances as low, medium or high presumed toxicity based on answers to a series of 33 questions, most about chemical structure. That paper remains an essential part of the concept of "thresholds of toxicological concern," which is a key component of the safety evaluation programs not only of the Expert Panel, but of the Joint FAO/WHO Expert Committee on Food Additives (JECFA) and other groups as well.

Beginning in the mid-1990s, global and regional flavor safety assessment programs such as those of JECFA and the European Union (now through the European Food Safety Authority, or EFSA) have been implemented using principles consistent with those of the FEMA GRAS assessment program; this has led to parallel results.

In the late 1990s it became apparent to the global flavor industry that the FEMA scientific program was the foundation for the industry's globalization efforts. The industry decided to adjust the program's financial support and management so they were shared more equally among members of the global flavor industry. Today, the International Organization of the Flavor Industry (IOFI), of which FEMA was a founding member in 1969, provides the financial support for the global flavor industry's scientific program. The program is managed by the IOFI Science Board. The FEMA Expert Panel remains independent under the sponsorship of FEMA.

The FEMA GRAS program has a rich history and heritage as a leader in the safety assessment of flavoring substances. The best evidence of the program's influence is the adoption by JECFA and EFSA of nearly all of the FEMA Expert Panel's flavor safety assessment techniques, and the fact that these groups' decisions on the safety of flavoring substances have been consistent with the GRAS determinations made by the FEMA Expert Panel.

With the scientific program begun by FEMA 50 years ago, and the independent FEMA Expert Panel, the global flavor industry can look forward to its next 50 years of leadership in assuring the safety of flavors.

Chapter 8
1970~1979

$\mathcal{T}$he social and political upheaval of the 1960s was followed by Watergate and the end of the Vietnam War in the 1970s. This decade also saw the birth of the environmental movement with the enactment of the first major piece of national environmental legislation, the National Environmental Policy Act (NEPA), on New Year's Day 1970. NEPA was followed by the first Earth Day on April 22, 1970, and the establishment of the Environmental Protection Agency in December 1970.

For the flavor industry, the 1970s presented a series of significant events and challenges, perhaps none more significant than the new flavor and food labeling regulations implemented by the Food and Drug Administration in 1973. The 1970s also saw the beginning of FEMA's collaboration with the FDA on the compilation of safety assessment information about flavoring substances, as the agency awarded FEMA a multi-year contract to prepare its Scientific Literature Reviews (SLRs). FEMA's first annual meeting of the decade took place at the Boca Raton Hotel and Racquet Club in Florida. Dr. Richard Hall of McCormick & Company, well on his way to becoming a central figure in FEMA's history, served as the association's president at the meeting. Hall became a champion of the flavor industry as president of FEMA and later as president of the Institute of Food Technologists, and acted as FEMA senior scientific advisor for more than 20 years.

The 1970 annual meeting also marked the development of the first comprehensive poundage and use survey of flavor ingredients used by the industry. The architects of the study, led by Dr. Jack Krum, chairman of the FEMA Food Additives Committee, set out to establish the conditions of intended use of the flavor ingredients employed by the industry. The survey was conducted in conjunction with the National Academy of Sciences and was sponsored by the FDA. It covered nearly 1,500 substances and became an integral part of FEMA's GRAS (generally recognized as safe) assessment program. Today, FEMA sponsors and conducts its own poundage surveys, sharing the results with the FDA and other regulators.

Early in the decade, the FDA proposed food and flavor labeling regulations that would have a major effect on

the industry. Initial proposals would have required food manufacturers to list the individual ingredients of a flavor on the product label, resulting in labels bigger than the food product in some instances. Such labeling would also have compromised trade secret flavor formulas. FEMA representatives appeared before Congress to testify that full disclosure was unnecessary and impractical.

"To firms in the flavor industry, their formulas are absolutely vital," said Bruce Durling, chairman of Stange. "Formulas are the embodiment of our creative response to the needs and demands of customers and consumers in a competitive market economy. Formulas are what we have to sell [to] our customers."

Durling's efforts were complemented by FEMA's Legislative Committee under the leadership of Gene Grisanti, president of International Flavors & Fragrances Inc. (IFF), as the members worked toward what they called "rectifying a misconception" by Congress about the safety and security of artificial flavors.

As the FDA developed its flavor and food labeling proposals, FEMA helped the agency understand the complexities of flavor manufacturing. A key point was that even though a flavor formula might consist of as

many as 100 flavoring substances, each of the individual substances would have been thoroughly evaluated for safety under its conditions of intended use; because of the demonstrated safety of these substances, there was no need to specifically identify each one on a product label.

Once the FDA regulations were finalized and published, FEMA went to work helping its members understand the regulations and their obligations for compliance. The new regulations were discussed in meetings and seminars, and in 1974 FEMA published its Flavor Labeling Handbook containing all of the regulations and other documents to help members understand them. The Handbook remains a useful document today. The FDA's flavor and food labeling regulations first promulgated in 1973 can be found today, largely unchanged, in the Code of Federal Regulations at 21 CFR 101.22.

Because of concern over the safety of the sweetener cyclamate and some other food ingredients, in the early 1970s President Richard Nixon appointed a special committee,

the Select Committee on GRAS Substances (SCOGS), to review the safety of substances that were "generally recognized as safe." Once again, FEMA led the way for the flavor industry by sharing scientific information on flavoring substances with the SCOGS. Because of FEMA's work, the committee decided that very few flavoring substances required a separate review.

It was FEMA's role in developing and growing the "FEMA GRAS" concept that firmly established the association's credibility and earned it international recognition as a scientific, policy-making body. Even federal regulatory officials acknowledged FEMA's contributions. "With the help of sterling characters like Dick Hall we're finally off and running on the President's directed review of the substances on the GRAS list," said Dale Lindsay, associate commissioner for science for the FDA. By 1976, the FDA recognized FEMA's GRAS lists in the Federal Register. Throughout the rest of the decade, the FDA would pay close attention to each succeeding publication of FEMA's GRAS data.

The FDA had regarded FEMA as a source of information on flavors and relied on its opinions of GRAS substances since the 1960s. But after FEMA completed its first poundage and use survey — and subsequently made plans for a re-review of all flavor ingredients by its Expert Panel — Dr. Robert Angelotti, director of the Office of Compliance and Bureau of Foods for the FDA, approached FEMA to ask if it would be willing to produce monographs

continued on page 113

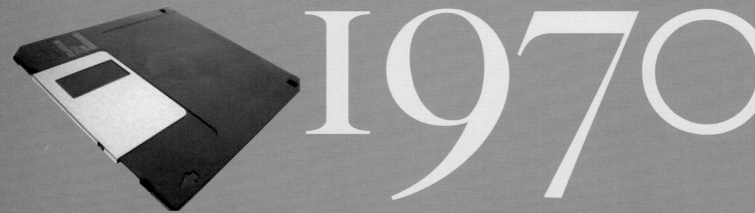

1970

IBM introduces the first computer floppy disk.

1971

The Hazard Analysis Critical Control Point (HACCP) system is presented at the National Conference on Food Protection, based on earlier work by the National Aeronautics and Space Administration, Pillsbury Company, and the U.S. Army to enhance processed food quality and safety for astronauts.

A computer system is developed to compare unknown spectra with a library of known mass spectra, eliminating the need for chemists to manually interpret the large number of spectra typically generated in a GC-MS analysis.

1972

Paul Berg, a Stanford University biochemist, produces the first recombinant DNA molecules by splicing together DNA from the SV40 virus and E. coli.

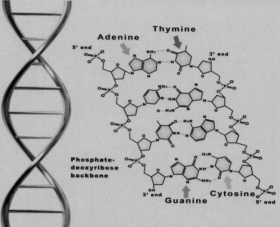

Adenine Thymine

5' end 3' end

Phosphate-deoxyribose backbone

3' end 5' end

Guanine Cytosine

1973

United States begins withdrawing from Vietnam.

1975

Bill Gates and Paul Allen launch Microsoft just after the first personal computer, the Altair 8800, is introduced by Micro Instrumentation and Telemetry Systems (MITS).

1977

International Federation of Essential Oils & Aroma Trades (IFEAT) is founded at the International Congress of Essential Oils in Kyoto, Japan.

1977

Max Winter identifies 2-methyl-4-propyl-1, 3-oxathiane as a character impact compound in passion fruit.

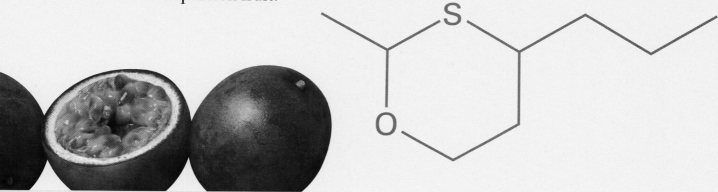

1979

Invention of the fused silica gas chromatography column provides increased strength and flexibility.

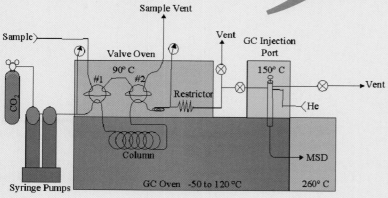

continued from page 107

on flavor substances — the SLRs. The FDA contracted with FEMA to produce the SLRs for the agency, and they remain available today through the National Technical Information Service.

A number of member companies contributed technical support to the FEMA Safety Evaluation Coordination Committee (SECC), which championed the SLR project and set guidelines and budgets for the review programs. The SLR project marked the beginning of the working relationship between FEMA and Dr. Timothy B. Adams. Adams has served FEMA on many projects as a consultant since the 1970s and has been FEMA's scientific director since 2001.

The SLRs served to formalize and document a key aspect of the safety assessments done by the FEMA Expert Panel — the evaluation of individual flavoring substances as members of structurally related groups. Also providing significant support for

FLAVOR AND EXTRACT MANUFACTURERS'
ASSOCIATION OF THE UNITED STATES

5th Annual

FALL SYMPOSIUM

Thursday, October 17, 1974
The Statler Hilton Hotel
Federal Room
Washington, D.C.

this important concept was the publication of the "Decision Tree," which would become a standard tool for assessing the safety of flavoring substances and other food ingredients. As Hall reported to members just before the Decision Tree's publication in Food and Cosmetic Toxicology in 1978, "It has had considerable field trials to test the ruggedness, the relevance, and reliability. Those people who have put it through its paces have been rather pleased with the results." Media accounts about the potentially harmful effects of food and color additives and flavors, like the Red Dye No. 2 and saccharin scares, brought flavor safety into prominent view, often with an unsubstantiated negative bent.

Dr. Richard V. Lechowich, head of the Food, Science, and Technology Department at Virginia Polytechnic Institute and a noted food scientist, spoke candidly about this issue at the 1978 FEMA Fall Symposium. While he noted that he was a "card-carrying member" of several nutritional and consumer organizations, he emphasized that the average person was many more times likely to perish from a lightning strike — or exposure to cancer-causing cosmic rays on a transcontinental flight — than from drinking one diet soda with saccharin per day.

Through scientific initiatives and its activist role in the food safety arena, FEMA found itself in a unique position. It had the capability to reassure American consumers who doubted the safety of their food supply.

Lacking a direct line of communication with consumers, FEMA's message of reassurance was most often conveyed through the FDA and food companies.

A key figure in FEMA history also began his tenure with the association in the 1970s: Dr. Richard A. Ford. Hired to work on the SLR project, Ford would serve FEMA for more than five years as a consultant, and then as scientific director. Ford and Hall co-authored the 1978 Decision Tree paper along with Greg Cramer of the FDA. Ford also played an important role in the development of the initial scientific and regulatory programs of the Geneva, Switzerland-based International Organization of the Flavor Industry (IOFI), founded in 1969. He served as a liaison between FEMA and IOFI and fostered the sharing of information related to flavor legislation and safety evaluation.

On the technical front, gas chromatography had become a major analytical tool by the 1970s. Richard Potter, FEMA's Research Committee chairman and a senior leader at Givaudan, was one of the first flavorists to use the technique in research. He pioneered the process by developing a method of determining how additions of synthetic aromatic chemicals affected vanilla extract. Gas chromatography ultimately would enable the industry to conduct sophisticated research in cost-effective ways that simply weren't practical before.

Scientific breakthroughs occurred in other areas as well during the 1970s. FEMA's Vanilla Committee, which had been using the same basic methods to analyze vanilla extracts for at least two decades, adopted new techniques from French researchers who had shown that isotopic ratios could be used to determine the adulteration of vanilla extracts much more precisely. This research would grow in the 1980s and 1990s through a partnership with the University of Georgia,

World Health Organization (WHO)

which used the technique to authenticate not only vanillin found naturally occurring in vanilla extracts, but many other flavor materials.

The safety and standardization work FEMA was doing domestically was reinforced

Top: FAO and WHO provide assistance to developing countries so they can take full advantage of the Codex Alimentarius Commission's work; bottom: The Commission works to help facilitate world food trade.

at the global level through FAO/WHO's Codex Alimentarius, an international body that develops food standards and guidelines. It would become an important aspect of the association's international safety program in the 1990s and early 2000s. Although it was little more than a rumor in America when the 1970s began, the Codex had been in existence since 1963 and listed nearly 100 countries in its membership, including the United States. Dr. Otho Easterday of IFF was one of

the Codex's chief proponents; through his affiliation with several European groups, he was able to get FEMA research about flavor ingredient evaluation into the Codex's general circulation, leading to a long-term cross-pollination of ideas and innovation between the two bodies.

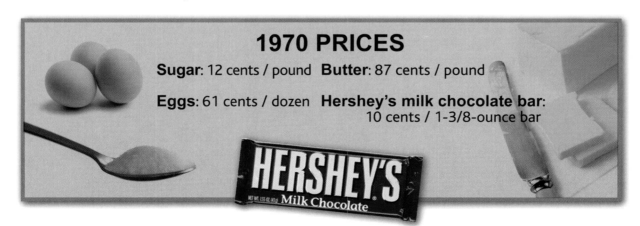

1970 PRICES

Sugar: 12 cents / pound **Butter**: 87 cents / pound

Eggs: 61 cents / dozen **Hershey's milk chocolate bar**: 10 cents / 1-3/8-ounce bar

Chapter 9
1980~1989

*I*n a decade in which FEMA would celebrate its 75th anniversary, the association was stretched to the limit by a series of legislative and regulatory initiatives on the state and federal levels. At the same time, consolidation increased in the flavor industry, altering the corporate footprints of many of the major flavor manufacturers. Wall Street analysts urged companies in many industries to get bigger as the best way to compete against large multinationals.

FEMA's regulatory challenges began in 1983 when the

Occupational Safety and Health Administration (OSHA) published the Hazard Communications Standard, a new regulation requiring that manufacturers of certain classes of substances — including flavors — provide detailed information to employees describing the possible hazards of substances in the workplace. All regulated substances were now required to have a material safety data sheet (MSDS) that described the physical and chemical properties of the substance and any potential human health hazards. Labeling requirements also meant that containers, piping and other vessels in manufacturing facilities had to be labeled for potential hazards.

The new regulation was particularly difficult for the flavor and fragrance manufacturing industries because they used so many substances in the formulation of their products. At the time, nearly 2,000 individual flavor and fragrance substances had been commercialized — and while many substances were of little safety concern, they were nonetheless covered by the new standard.

FEMA and its sister organization, the Fragrance Materials Association (FMA), joined forces to create a tool that companies in both industries could use as one aid for their compliance with the new standard. The result was the Flavor and Fragrance Ingredient Data Sheet (FFIDS). The FFIDS wasn't an MSDS, but companies could use the information in the FFIDSs as an important source to help them develop their own MSDSs. The FFIDSs have become an invaluable resource and remain in use by companies as one source of information, along with their own proprietary data, and material from various databases, that they use to develop their own MSDSs. The FFIDSs are updated regularly and remain available to all FEMA members through the database managed by FEMA and the Research Institute for Fragrance Materials (RIFM).

One of the biggest challenges of the Hazard Communications Standard was the tight two-year timeline that OSHA required for compliance. This meant that for the FFIDSs to be most helpful to FEMA's members, more than 2,000 individual FFIDSs had to be completed between 1983 and 1984 — a daunting task. By the time the $1 million project was done, successfully and on schedule, both FEMA and FMA had exhausted their budget surpluses to finance it. Much of the project was completed in FEMA's Washington, D.C., office. Dr. Tim Adams, FEMA's current scientific director, and John Hallagan, FEMA's current general counsel, both worked extensively on the FFIDS project under the direction of FEMA General Counsel and Executive Secretary Dan Thompson.

The flavor industry's ability to protect its valuable trade secret formula information was tested again in the 1980s, this time at the state level. In 1983, New Jersey passed the Worker and Community Right-To-Know Act, which required companies in the state to provide a substantial amount of information about the chemical composition of their products. As interpreted by state regulators, the act mandated that manufacturers disclose all flavor formulations for products produced and sold in New Jersey. With so much at stake and so many flavor companies based in the state, FEMA's members asked the association to do everything possible to help them protect their trade secrets.

FEMA went to court seeking to obtain a more favorable interpretation of the act. "It has been very rare over the years for FEMA to turn to the

The U.S. Senate chambers in Washington, D.C.

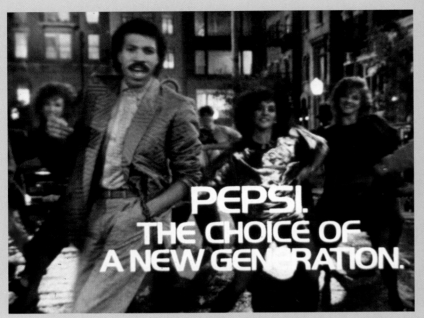

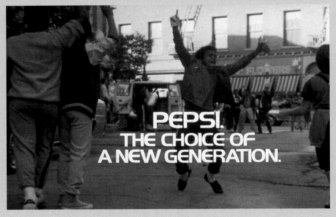

courts for regulatory relief, but in this instance the potential harm to our members forced us to file an injunction in the federal courts," said Hallagan. "In fact, we took the case all the way to the Supreme Court, where our appeal was ultimately denied."

FEMA then worked with state regulators to create a workable system that would meet the requirements of the law while still protecting flavor companies' valuable trade secret formulas. With procedures in place that were agreeable to both the flavor manufacturers and the regulators, flavor manufacturers dutifully provided their flavor formulas to the state. The result — as FEMA had warned — was a massive amount of paper that left state officials

scrambling to find additional storage space.

After several years of trying to manage the vast quantity of paper (electronic storage was still in its infancy) — and with a substantial amount of work from FEMA's newly hired director of government relations, Glenn Roberts, and industry volunteer Dr. Fred Stone of Firmenich — New Jersey reconsidered its position. In 1991, the state agreed to allow flavor manufacturers to take back the information without the state retaining copies, as long as the companies had implemented a state-mandated tracking system.

One of the few regulatory definitions of "natural" as it pertains to food is the definition of "natural flavor" in the Food and Drug Administration's regulations at

21 CFR 101.22(a)(3). This definition was promulgated by FDA in the early 1970s, and by the 1980s it became clear that the definition was being interpreted in a variety of ways within the flavor and food industries, with questions about how "natural" certain flavoring substances were. Issues associated with the "naturalness" of a key flavoring substance, benzaldehyde, helped to bring things to a head.

Benzaldehyde is often employed, in its natural or synthetic form, to provide a characteristic cherry flavor to a variety of flavor formulations used in beverages and other foods. When a supplier of "natural" benzaldehyde started contacting the FDA to assert the "naturalness" of its benzaldehyde, FEMA got involved. Under the leadership of FEMA presidents Dr. Jim Broderick of H. Kohnstamm (1986) and Bill Downey of Fritzsche, Dodge & Olcott (1987),

the association established a special subcommittee of the Flavor Labeling Committee to study the issue of using newly developed, sophisticated analytical methods to verify the naturalness of flavoring substances.

The Isotopic Studies Committee (ISC), as it became known, managed a research program at the University of Georgia that led to the development of new analytical methods still used today to verify that flavor substances are derived from natural sources. Since then, researchers at the university have published a number of papers in the scientific literature, not only broadening the field of discourse but also inspiring other scientists to dig deeper into the origins of flavors and other food ingredients.

FEMA also conducted an extensive evaluation of the FDA definition of natural flavor codified at 21 CFR 101.22(a)(3) by forming four task forces under the direction of Downey to examine the key areas of the definition: starting

continued on page 124

FEMA celebrated its 75th anniversary in 1984 during its annual meeting at Marco Island Resort in Florida.

1981

Maryvonne and Gérard Martin develop the SNIF (Site-Specific Natural Isotope Fractionation) NMR technique. Originally used to determine the origin of wines, this technique is now one of many, such as enantioselective capillary GC or isotope ratio mass spectrometry, used to ensure the naturalness of food ingredients.

1982

E. Demole identifies 1-p-Menthene-8-thiol as a character impact compound in grapefruit juice. Very powerful with an odor threshold of 0.0001 ppb, it also requires stabilization as it tends to rapidly cyclize to the thio analog of dihydropinol.

1985

FDA approves irradiation to control *Trichinella spiralis* in pork.

Coca-Cola announces a new taste for Coke, then responds to Americans' emotional attachment for the original formula, returning it as Coca-Cola classic®.

1986

FDA approves irradiation to disinfest and/or delay ripening in some fresh fruits and vegetables, and to control microorganisms in spices and herbs.

1987

New York Stock Exchange suffers
huge drop on "Black Monday."

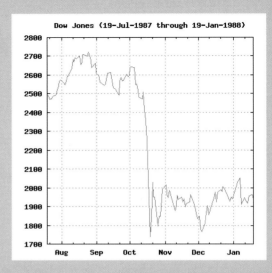

Dow Jones (19-Jul-1987 through 19-Jan-1988)

1988

KRAFT ®

Philip Morris Companies purchases Kraft for $12.9 billion.

1989

Kraft merges with Philip Morris's General
Foods unit as Kraft General Foods.

Berlin Wall falls.

1989

BETONDEMONTAGETE

LOVE & PEACE

Test West

In 1985, FEMA Expert Panel members gathered in New York for the panel's 25th anniversary: (back row, from left) Bob Smith, Richard Ford (liaison member from RIFM and former Expert Panel executive secretary), Bernard Wagner and Philip Portoghese; (front row, from left) Lauren Woods, Carrol Weil, Bernard Oser (founder and non-voting chairman) and Paul Newberne. (Not pictured: Expert Panel member John Doull)

continued from page 119

materials, physical processes, chemical processes and new technologies. Among the participants in the task forces were Klaus Bauer (Dragoco — now Symrise), Dr. Otho Easterday (IFF), Dr. Richard Hall (McCormick & Company), Dr. Chuck Manley (Takasago), and Dick Pisano Sr. (Citrus and Allied) — all of whom have since received the Dr. Richard L. Hall Distinguished Service Award.

The association celebrated another auspicious milestone in 1985 when it marked the 25th anniversary of the FEMA Expert Panel. All current and former panel members who were available convened at a special event at Windows on the World restaurant in New York City's World Trade Center on April 2, 1985. It's doubtful there has ever been such a collection of scientific talent in a single room at one time throughout the association's history.

At the time, Hall looked back fondly on the Expert Panel's early safety evaluation work and its impact on the industry: "The FDA, after its first attempt at publication of a GRAS list, literally threw up its hands and said it did not know how to handle the remaining flavor substances. Our program permitted the small but steady introduction of carefully evaluated new substances . . ."

There was a significant changing of the guard just a year later, when the Expert Panel's founder and first chairman, Dr. Bernard Oser, retired. Oser, who passed away in 1997, left behind a legacy of tireless service on behalf of the flavor industry. But it was his vision in establishing the Expert Panel and guiding it through its formative years that

124

"Grandpa, where do flavors come from?"

From us, of course.

David Michael & Co., Inc.
Our flavors bring food products to life.

HOME OFFICE: 10801 Decatur Road, Philadelphia, PA 19154
215-632-3100   TWX: 710-670-1014, MICHAELS PHA

Offices also in: Paramount, Calif.   Northbrook, IL   Mississauga, Ontario, Canada
Herkserm, Belgium   Rio Piedras, Puerto Rico   Tokyo, Japan   Victoria, Australia

A 1980s ad for David Michael & Co., Inc., featured Walter Rosskam and his grandson Andrew,
the son of Skip Rosskam (FEMA president from 2003 to 2004).

Top: FEMA members enjoy a fish fry hosted by International Flavors & Fragrances Inc. after a Safety Evaluation Coordination Committee meeting in Aspen, Colo., during the 1980s; bottom right: Otho Easterday, chair of the FEMA SECC, and his wife, Sue.

ensured his place in FEMA history.

The Expert Panel published two compilations of new FEMA GRAS flavoring substances in 1984 and 1985, adding 104 new flavor ingredients to the list. By 1989, approximately 1,750 flavor ingredients had been "generally recognized as safe" (GRAS), thanks to the efforts of the FEMA Expert Panel.

The 1980s were also characterized by a period of great scientific growth. Traditional toxicology was being augmented by new technologies enabling scientists to focus more on actual mechanisms of toxicity rather than simply the obvious effects on rats and mice. Also during the 1980s, the first significant advances in computer technology were occurring. By 1983, FEMA was exploring the possibility of computerizing its database on flavor ingredients. During the 1980s FEMA began the development of what has become the FEMA/RIFM database on flavor and fragrance substances. "It felt like an era of breakthroughs," said Manley, a former FEMA president, who also led several committees during the 1980s. "We applied the new knowledge we gained from the scientific evolution as fast as we could to the safety research we were conducting."

Meanwhile, FEMA scientists developed the "consumption ratio," which remains a useful tool to compare the intake of flavoring substances from natural food sources with the intake from added flavors. Led by Dr. Jan Stofberg of the PFW Company (later Tastemaker), the researchers collected data on hundreds of GRAS substances, facilitating an analysis of the priority that should be assigned for safety evaluation. Stofberg would later receive the Dr. Richard L. Hall Distinguished Service Award for his contribution.

The Safety Evaluation Coordination Committee (SECC) was primarily responsible for managing FEMA's scientific program in the 1980s. Chaired by Easterday of IFF, the SECC addressed a number of issues facing the industry, including the interpretation of a key National Toxicology Program (NTP) bioassay on benzyl acetate, an evaluation of the implications of the

NTP bioassay of d-limonene, and the start of extensive study programs for process flavors and anethole.

During the 1980s, FEMA had three people fill the role of scientific director for the association.

Dr. Richard Ford served as scientific director from 1974-1981, Bruce Bernard took over from 1981-1985, and George Burdock was scientific director from 1985-1992.

FEMA PROPOSED FISCAL YEAR 1983-1984 EXPENDITURES BY FUNCTION

SAFETY EVALUATION 61%
Expert Panel, Testing Program, Food Additives and Technical Committees, Safety Evaluation Coordination Committee

GOVERNMENT RELATIONS* 16%
Legislative and Regulatory Activities, IOFI/Codex, Other Committee Activities

ANNUAL MEETINGS AND MEMBERSHIP COMMUNICATIONS 13%

GENERAL OPERATIONS 8%

2% CONTINGENCY

*A significant amount of the Government Relations budget is expected to be spent on matters related to safety evaluation.

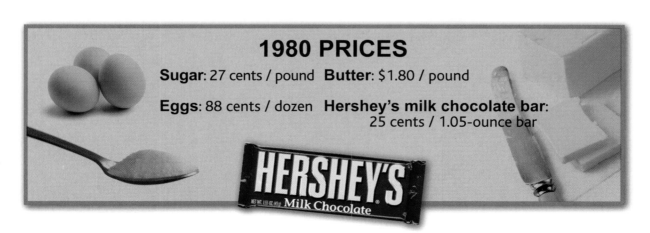

1980 PRICES

Sugar: 27 cents / pound   **Butter:** $1.80 / pound

Eggs: 88 cents / dozen   **Hershey's milk chocolate bar:** 25 cents / 1.05-ounce bar

HERSHEY'S Milk Chocolate

Chapter 10
1990~1999

A decade that began with the launch of the Hubble Space Telescope and the first Gulf War also saw the impact of the North American Free Trade Agreement as U.S. cross-border trade with Mexico and Canada became even easier. Political upheaval internationally and domestically dominated the news. The go-go economy of the '90s generated an all-time high in the stock market and a period of sustained prosperity for Americans.

In the flavor business, consolidation became the recurring headline as more and more manufacturers joined together, recognizing economies of scale in product development and production. International Flavors & Fragrances Inc. (IFF), Givaudan and Firmenich, Inc., three big global players, increased their reach through the acquisition of smaller, well-established firms. Consolidation in the food and beverage industry also contributed to a more global view of product marketing.

The advent of core supplier lists from key clients drove many flavor companies to look for more economical means to produce flavors. The global reach of American companies increased, as did the presence of international firms in the United States. Yet as always, smaller players, often with deep roots in the industry, found niches where they could compete with much larger firms as they offered unique products, exceptional service or significant value to clients.

Increasingly, players on the global stage began to see the need for more harmonious regulations. For FEMA members, with decades of experience and confidence in the GRAS approach for safety evaluation, it was a matter of principle and business expediency to promote FEMA's scientific methods to support flavor safety assessment internationally.

A worldwide patchwork of negative lists, positive lists, mixed lists, and no lists at all led to a concern that without FEMA's direct involvement, flavor safety assessment could fall to the lowest common denominator — or vary so widely by country or region that international trade would be compromised. Many of FEMA's smaller member companies also recognized that if a substance was banned in one part of the world because of ill-informed public clamor and poor to no science, then U.S. customer companies would remove the substance from their ingredient lists.

One event that galvanized FEMA to take a more active role globally was the 1992 evaluation of an important flavoring substance, furfural, by the Joint FAO/WHO Expert Committee on Food Additives (JECFA). JECFA conducted its evaluation of furfural as a typical food additive, and as a result, requested voluminous additional safety data that were largely irrelevant to furfural's use as a flavoring substance. This led FEMA to work with the Food and Drug Administration to address the U.S. flavor industry's concerns about JECFA's safety evaluation procedures for flavoring substances.

Recognizing the increased globalization of the market for flavors, FEMA adopted a goal of creating a safety assessment procedure that would lead to a globally recognized, harmonized list of safe, "approved" flavoring substances. The first discussion of ways to reach this goal took place at a meeting of FEMA's Safety Evaluation Coordination Committee (SECC) in Aspen, Colo., in July 1992, following the JECFA evaluation of furfural.

FEMA's many years of cooperation with the FDA had created an environment of mutual trust and credibility, through the work of the independent FEMA Expert Panel and the association's own tradition of proactive efforts on behalf of flavor safety. FEMA supported the

FDA in its initial discussions with JECFA in 1992-93, and later as JECFA considered a procedure to evaluate flavor safety during 1994 and 1995. In 1996, JECFA adopted and published a new safety assessment procedure based largely on the FEMA approach, and in the years since has accepted the vast majority of FEMA GRAS flavoring substances that it has evaluated. After the new JECFA safety evaluation procedure was adopted, the FDA began providing a group of flavoring substances for JECFA to evaluate each year.

During the late 1990s, FEMA led a number of key discussions to promote the globalization of flavor safety assessment and regulations. Recognizing the financial

Eastwell Manor in England, site of a key meeting with FEMA and flavor associations from around the world about how to make IOFI more effective

impact of the industry's global harmonization goals, FEMA worked with the International Organization of the Flavor Industry (IOFI) and the global flavor industry in assessing an equitable way to share funding responsibility. The IOFI Zero Based Task Force was a first step toward a new approach to funding science to promote the safety of flavors worldwide.

One key meeting was held in 1998 at Eastwell Manor, a stately hotel in the south of England. The meeting brought together representatives of FEMA and flavor associations from around the world to begin discussions on how to make IOFI a more effective organization.

The gathering had far-reaching results including the development of the IOFI Red Book, which outlined IOFI's roles and responsibilities. "This was a groundbreaking meeting for the global flavor industry as we mapped out future cooperation and collaboration among global companies and national associations in sharing information on emerging regulatory trends and scientific developments, and funding a global scientific program," remembers John Hallagan, then FEMA's scientific director and a participant in the Eastwell Manor meeting.

In addition to safety assessment, product labeling began to emerge as a major issue for FEMA members. The trade secrets of individual flavor companies were at risk as labeling regulations around the globe began to threaten the disclosure of component ingredients or formulas.

Domestically, the 1990 Nutrition Labeling and Education Act (NLEA) had far-reaching impact through the decade, as the FDA began a concerted effort to encourage consumers to be more aware of the nutritional content of foods and beverages.

FEMA had been successful in addressing labeling laws in New Jersey and California that otherwise would have violated the trade secrets of its members. "FEMA and member companies worked effectively with government agencies and customers to find the level of confidential disclosure necessary to address their needs while protecting the intellectual property of our industry," recalls Fred Stults, FEMA's president in 1997.

By successfully petitioning the state of New Jersey about the New Jersey Right to Know Act in 1991, FEMA was able to have nearly 50,000 trade secrets returned. Mid-decade, FEMA's effective guidance helped reduce the impact on the flavor industry of Proposition 65, a new California regulation requiring warning labels on consumer products that contained certain substances found to be hazardous by the state. FEMA continued its valuable member support by assuring the safety of flavoring substances, while helping its members protect their trade secrets.

In 1995, in recognition of an industry pioneer's significant contributions, FEMA's board of directors created the Dr. Richard L. Hall Distinguished Service Award to honor those who have demonstrated exceptional service and commitment, resulting in significant and lasting contributions to the flavor industry. Presented only in years when a deserving candidate has been identified, the first Distinguished Service Award was given to Dr. Richard Hall himself.

In 1996, the FDA began to address an emerging problem it described as "undeclared allergens in food." Existing FDA policy had allowed for two types of exemptions: one for spices, flavors and colors and the other for incidental additives. The FDA had already announced publicly that the Food, Drug, and Cosmetic Act allowed spices, flavors and colors to be declared collectively without naming each one. Because in some instances those ingredients contained sub-components that were allergens, the FDA strongly encouraged the declaration of any allergenic ingredient contained in a spice, flavor or color.

As a result of these FDA policies, FEMA conducted several labeling and allergen workshops to ensure compliance with the FDA regulations.

This was also a decade of great progress for FEMA on the scientific front, as the association supported studies of process flavor ingredients and

continued on page 137

Nutrition Facts

Nutrition Facts	Amount/serving	%DV*	Amount/serving	%DV*
Serv. Size 1 cup (249g)	Total Fat 12g	18%	Sodium 940mg	39%
	Sat. Fat 6g	30%	Total Carb. 24g	8%
Servings About 2	Polyunsat. Fat 1.5g		Dietary Fiber 1g	4%
Calories 250 Fat Cal. 110	Monounsat. Fat 2.5g		Sugars 1g	
*Percent Daily Values (DV) are based on a 2,000 calorie diet.	Cholest. 60mg	20%	Protein 10g	20%
	Vitamin A 0% • Vitamin C 0% • Calcium 6% • Iron 8%			

INGREDIENTS: WATER, CHICKEN STOCK, ENRICHED PASTA (SEMOLINA WHEAT FLOUR, EGG WHITE SOLIDS, NIACIN, IRON, THIAMIN MONONITRATE [VITAMIN B1], RIBOFLAVIN [VITAMIN B2] AND FOLIC ACID), CREAM (DERIVED FROM MILK), CHICKEN, CONTAINS LESS THAN 2% OF CHEESES (GRANULAR, PARMESAN AND ROMANO PASTE [PASTEURIZED COW'S MILK, CULTURES, SALT, ENZYMES], WATER, SALT, LACTIC ACID, CITRIC ACID AND DISODIUM PHOSPHATE), BUTTER (PASTEURIZED CREAM [DERIVED FROM MILK] AND SALT), MODIFIED CORN STARCH, WHOLE EGG SOLIDS, SUGAR, DATEM, RICE STARCH, GARLIC, XANTHAN GUM, CHEESE FLAVOR (PARTIALLY HYDROGENATED SOYBEAN OIL, FLAVORINGS AND SMOKE FLAVORING), MUSTARD FLOUR, ISOLATED SOY PROTEIN AND SODIUM PHOSPHATE.

Nutrition Facts

Serving Size 1 potato (148g/5.3oz)

Amount Per Serving

Calories 100 — Calories from Fat 0

	% Daily Value*
Total Fat 0g	0%
Saturated Fat 0g	0%
Cholesterol 0mg	0%
Sodium 0mg	0%
Potassium 720mg	21%
Total Carbohydrate 26g	9%
Dietary Fiber 3g	12%
Sugars 3g	
Protein 4g	

Vitamin A 0%	•	Vitamin C 45%	
Calcium 2%	•	Iron 6%	
Thiamin 8%	•	Riboflavin 2%	
Niacin 8%	•	Vitamin B₆ 10%	
Folate 6%	•	Phosphorous 6%	
Zinc 2%	•	Magnesium 6%	

*Percent Daily Values are based on a 2,000 calorie diet.

1990

FDA approves irradiation to control
harmful bacteria in fresh and frozen poultry.

1991

The Soviet Union collapses.

1993

Ohmic heating (passing an electrical current through food to heat it
rapidly to a sterilizing temperature) is approved by the FDA to process
stable low-acid food at ambient temperature.

1994

First rDNA-engineered plant food, a tomato with delayed ripening called the Flavr Savr, is commercially introduced by Calgene.

1995

FDA mandates Hazard Analysis Critical Control Point (HACCP) food safety program for fish and fishery products.

1996

Mad cow disease hits Great Britain.

1996

Steam pasteurization and vacuuming of beef carcasses introduced to reduce microbial hazards.

USDA mandates HACCP for meat and poultry products.

Scientists create the first mammal to be cloned with DNA taken from an adult cell—a sheep named for country singer Dolly Parton.

1997

FDA approves irradiation to control harmful bacteria in red meats.

1998

Pasteurized Eggs, L.P. develops the first commercial pasteurization process for shell eggs.

High pressure processing (using hydrostatic pressure of 50,000 to 100,000 psi) is commercially applied to fresh packaged foods to kill spoilage microorganisms without altering flavor, appearance or nutritional value.

Grain products are first fortified with folic acid.

1999

The discovery of G protein-coupled receptors in the taste buds of the rat and mouse by Dr. Mark Hoon et al. leads ultimately to the entire field of taste receptor science.

DR. RICHARD L. HALL
DISTINGUISHED SERVICE AWARD

1995
Richard L. Hall, Ph.D. – McCormick & Company

1996
J. Frank Perkins, Ph.D. – Firmenich, Inc.

1997
James J. Broderick, Ph.D. – H. Kohnstamm & Company

1998
Otho Easterday, Ph.D. – International Flavors & Fragrances Inc.

1999
Ian Stofberg, Ph.D. – PFW Aroma Chemicals

2000
Daniel R. Thompson – The Law Office of Daniel R. Thompson

2001
Fred W. Stone, Ph.D. – Firmenich, Inc.

2002
No award given

2003
Klaus Bauer – Symrise, Inc.

2004
James Emerson, D.V.M., Ph.D., and
Julia Howell – The Coca-Cola Company

2005
Daniel E. Stebbins – Symrise, Inc.

2006
Richard Pisano Sr. – Citrus and Allied Essences Ltd.

2007
Charles Manley, Ph.D. – Takasago International Corporation

2008
Fred H. Stults, Ph.D. - Givaudan

continued from page 131

anethole, and began a long project on the potential genotoxicity of certain flavoring substances. During the 1990s, the FEMA Expert Panel issued GRAS publications 15 through 18, describing 151 new FEMA GRAS flavoring substances. Longtime Expert Panel member Paul Newberne, one of the panel's most active chairmen, retired as the decade came to a close.

FEMA also made strides in updating the flavor information in the database it owned jointly with the fragrance industry; the database was managed by the Research Institute for Fragrance Materials (RIFM). The FEMA SLR/Database Task Force, chaired by Julia Howell of The Coca-Cola Company, managed the process of adding voluminous data on flavors to the database during the mid-1990s. This resulted in a current, state-of-the-art database on flavors. FEMA also worked to make the database more accessible to its members, increasing the value of FEMA membership.

In 1997, FEMA held its first workshop on respiratory health and safety in flavor manufacturing. This critically important initiative, which continued and grew in the 2000s, helped flavor manufacturers maintain the safest workplaces possible.

Throughout the 1990s, FEMA also stepped up education and member support with a series of workshops on other key topics like FEMA GRAS, hazard communications, intellectual property, flavor labeling, and food allergies.

FEMA committees were active throughout the decade too. The International Regulatory Affairs Committee (IRAC) tracked global regulatory developments and reported on them to members.

Served around the World

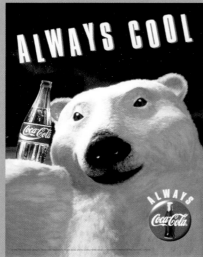

Committees convened regularly to address science and regulatory issues, labeling, FEMA membership, and methods of scientific analysis.

Increased member demand for information on a wide and growing list of topics resulted in an expansion of staff support. Dan Thompson, FEMA's long-time general counsel and executive secretary, made a number of changes in the 1990s to expand FEMA's capabilities.

Thompson hired Glenn Roberts in 1990 as FEMA's first director of government relations. Thompson also added professional meeting planning and management staff to meet FEMA's burgeoning needs. John Hallagan, FEMA's scientific director, employed several new scientists to work in FEMA's expanded scientific program, including Dr. Tim Adams, who had worked with FEMA during the 1970s and returned to the association as a consultant in 1992.

John Hallagan meets with Chinese food safety officer Dr. Yin Dakui in 1996.

Industry consolidation and downsizing resulted in a downturn in the number of industry volunteers able to work on FEMA initiatives. Individuals from FEMA member companies who had stepped forward to assist with committee and project work retired; this turnover in the FEMA volunteer ranks remains a challenge to the present day.

1990 PRICES

Sugar: 42 cents / pound **Butter**: $2.11 / pound

Eggs: $1.22 / dozen **Hershey's milk chocolate bar**: 45 cents / bar

Chapter 11
2000-2008

The new millennium began without a hitch, as frenzied Y2K concerns faded with no major impact on global technology. The contested presidential race of 2000 began a decade that ended with the historic election of Barack Obama as president on Nov. 4, 2008. In 2001, the 9/11 attacks on the World Trade Center and the Pentagon brought the entire world community closer for a time, as sympathy for the American victims of the tragedy engendered a sense of shared humanity. Wars in Afghanistan and Iraq, the disastrous explosion of the Space Shuttle *Columbia*, the cataclysmic impact of Hurricane Katrina, huge budget deficits and an economic meltdown joined to make Americans feel less certain about the future.

Trends in the flavor business that began in the 1980s and 1990s continued, with more acquisitions and consolidations among the global players, belt-tightening and budget concerns across the board, and continued resilience and growth for many smaller, family-owned businesses.

Dan Thompson, who had managed FEMA's operations for more than 30 years, retired in 2000. Following a well-developed succession plan, the association management transitioned to former Director of Government Relations Glenn Roberts, who was intimately familiar with flavor industry regulatory issues and association management, and John Hallagan, whose training in science and law had equipped him to provide leadership as FEMA's scientific director and legal adviser for most of the 1990s. The Roberts Group (TRG) became the primary provider of management and scientific services to FEMA.

Through the decade, FEMA staff at TRG expanded to include additional professionals who support the association's science, advocacy and member communication. Cathy Cook, John Cox, Christie Lucas Gavin, MJ Marshall, Jane Reynolds and Sean Taylor joined the FEMA staff, adding depth and breadth of services available to members.

At the turn of this century, a progressive FEMA board involved members in charting a strategic direction for the association. Part of the project included extensive member surveys, with an aim of identifying any gaps between the board and the membership in terms of understanding critical issues and direction. "As a result of these strategic planning initiatives, FEMA focused on four major strategic areas: safety through science, advocacy, intellectual property protection, and communication," recalls Mike Davis, FEMA president in 2000-2001.

At this time, FEMA also discovered that the value of many years of scientific support for ingredient safety and long-running advocacy efforts was not necessarily understood by all members. Increasingly, members needed to justify the FEMA dues expense to management who often came from backgrounds outside of the flavor business. "FEMA efforts through the 2000s continued to demonstrate the high value of membership across all segments of the industry, from family owned to multinational flavor houses and ingredient suppliers as well as consumer product companies," noted Arthur J. Schick Jr., vice president, Purchasing, Pepsi-Cola Concentrate Operations, and FEMA treasurer in 2008.

Increased globalization in the flavor business and stepped-up regulation internationally had begun in the 1990s. By the 2000s, it became even more important for FEMA to leverage its years of safety assessment leadership and understanding of complex flavor regulation to support a more globally harmonized approach to the safety evaluation and regulation of flavors.

Working with other members of the International Organization of the Flavor Industry (IOFI), FEMA encouraged changes that would help IOFI assume the role of global leader in scientific issues affecting the flavor industry.

Consistent with an approach begun in the 1990s, FEMA continued to work with the Food and Drug Administration to support the worldwide safety assessment body Joint FAO/WHO Expert Committee on Food Additives (JECFA) as it addressed

With more than 150 years of combined service to FEMA, The Roberts Group professionals include (seated in front row, left to right): Glenn Roberts, executive director; Christie Lucas Gavin, MPH, health and safety director; MJ Marshall, government relations director; Cathy Cook, communications director; Jane Reynolds, meetings & member services director; John B. Hallagan, general counsel; Greer B. Gilka, client finances director; and John H. Cox, assistant general counsel; (standing in back row, left to right): Sean V. Taylor, Ph.D., assistant scientific director; Timothy B. Adams, Ph.D., scientific director; Margaret M. McGowen, Ph.D., staff scientist; and Michelle C. Williams, M.S., staff scientist.

the treatment of flavors in global food standards through the Codex Alimentarius Commission.

FEMA amplified its voice through a cooperative effort with other IOFI member associations. Codex adopted its Guidelines on Flavours in 2008, a global standard for the regulation of flavors that was largely consistent with the program originally conceived by FEMA. This accomplishment means that the JECFA method of flavor safety evaluation is consistent with the methods employed by the FEMA GRAS program, making the latter a central part of the platform for global harmonization.

With globalization came a rapid growth of materials requiring safety assessments. Science funding became a critical issue. The FEMA scientific program had become the cornerstone of global safety evaluations, and in 2005, much of the FEMA program became IOFI's global scientific program, when the IOFI board agreed that IOFI member associations around the world and several large multinational companies would shoulder the financial burden for this critical

and significantly expanded global scientific work. The new approach preserved the FEMA Expert Panel's independence while providing resources — both financial and professional expertise — to conduct the safety assessments needed globally. At this time, the scientific staff of The Roberts Group who served FEMA essentially became the IOFI scientific staff. At the same time, FEMA ensured that the TRG staff also capably handled the purely domestic scientific and regulatory questions of its members.

FEMA's Expert Panel was also active through this decade in developing and publishing criteria for single chemically defined flavoring substances, and in codifying the safety assessment methodology for natural essential oils and extractives. The procedure for the safety evaluation of natural extractives, termed the "Natural Paradigm," used FEMA's extensive experience

with structure-activity relationships (see Chapter 8) to support a rational approach to this complex challenge. Also developed during this decade was the efficient and cost-effective "Group GRAS" program that allowed new chemically similar flavoring substances to be evaluated together as structurally related groups.

From 2000 to 2009, the Expert Panel published six reports announcing the FEMA GRAS status of more than 500 new flavoring substances. The 2000s also saw the retirement of John Doull, a key member of the Expert Panel for many years.

FEMA continued its efforts to support accurate exposure-based safety evaluation by conducting poundage surveys. A far cry from the manual punch card technique employed by FEMA 40 years earlier, the 2005 FEMA poundage survey was the most thorough ever, and used cutting-edge technology that allowed the research to be conducted electronically. IOFI looked to FEMA for its

insight and expertise when IOFI planned the first-ever global poundage survey of flavor materials in 2008.

In recognition of the work of key individuals for the advancement of science in the industry, FEMA established the Excellence in Flavor Science Award in 2006. The award recognizes individuals who have shown outstanding dedication to the advancement of flavor science by conducting original research and publishing articles on the topics of flavor chemistry, biochemistry, physiology, molecular biology, and biotechnology. To date, recipients of the award have been:

* 2006: Gary Reineccius, Ph.D. — The University of Minnesota
* 2007: Regula Näf, Ph.D. — Firmenich International SA, Switzerland
* 2008: Prof. Peter Schieberle, Ph.D. — Technische Universität München, Germany

FEMA continued to address another major challenge to the industry that began in the late 1990s: respiratory health and safety in flavor manufacturing. Concerns related to the manufacture of butter-flavored microwave popcorn brought this issue into full public view with unprecedented media coverage of FEMA and the flavor industry.

FEMA conducted three extensive workshops for flavor and food manufacturing companies in 2002, 2005 and

continued on page 146

Scientific advancements in the laboratory helped propel the flavor industry into the first decade of the new millennium.

Photo courtesy of Givaudan

143

2000

University of Miami scientists discover and isolate a taste receptor on the tongue for umami, the "fifth taste," found in soy sauce, ripe tomatoes, mushrooms and other foods.

2001

Terrorists attack the World Trade Center in New York City and the Pentagon in Arlington County, Va.

Hong Kong orders more than 1 million chickens and other poultry killed to halt the spread of a major bird flu epidemic.

2005

Hurricane Katrina slams into the U.S. Gulf Coast, displacing a million people and killing almost 1,800.

2007

Two teams of scientists, one in Wisconsin and the other in Japan, announce they have discovered a way to make embryonic stem cells from skin cells.

2008

The United States and the world face the worst economic crisis since the Depression, resulting in massive government intervention in financial systems globally.

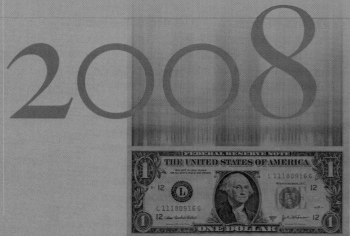

Photo courtesy of www.BurwellPhotography.com and www.gpi.org

146

continued from page 143

2007, and in 2004, published the report "Respiratory Health and Safety in the Flavor Manufacturing Workplace," which became the key reference for the industry and regulators alike. Also unprecedented in the history of FEMA was the association's inclusion as a defendant in a number of lawsuits brought by workers in microwave popcorn and flavor manufacturing. FEMA's strong history of proactively addressing these issues resulted in FEMA's dismissal from every lawsuit.

As John Hallagan, FEMA's general counsel, noted, "The legal community, the media and regulators all have recognized that FEMA took a powerful leadership role in helping flavor and food manufacturers to have the safest workplaces possible even before state and federal regulators began their efforts."

Another trend impacting the flavor industry was growing consumer interest in organic products and flavors as well as larger markets for kosher and halal products. Expansion of these product lines has had a significant impact on procurement and manufacturing

processes in the flavor industry.

In 2006, FEMA measured progress in its strategic areas, once again incorporating the voices of members through interviews and surveys. The new strategic plan reflected business and regulatory realities. Key issues identified by members late in the decade included maintaining and enhancing membership value through education, access to professional resources and information, and a balance between FEMA's leadership on global flavor safety issues and focus on its North American base of companies and strong relationship with the FDA.

Late in this decade, FEMA also realigned its committee structure. The FEMA Regulatory Affairs Committee (FRAC) replaced the International Regulatory Affairs Committee (IRAC) and continued to lead efforts to communicate the fast developing regulatory changes both inside

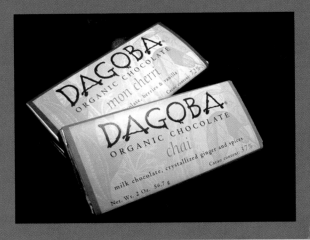

think5™
RED BERRY FLAVOR

3 cups vegetables & 2 cups fruit for delicious nutrition on-the-go

gluten free
omega-3
high in fiber

5 cup bar

NET WT 2.53 OZ (72g)

JORDANS
FAMILY MILLERS SINCE 1855
JORDANS
ORGANIC MUESLi
Raw & Toasted British Wholegrains
with HAZELNUTS
JUICY RAISINS
SULTANAS
& sunflower
Grown by nature. Crafted by Jordans.

GEAR UP FOR THE GOLD
2008 BEIJING
REDEEM POINTS FOR OROWEAT TEAM USA GEAR!
New!
OROWEAT.
Whole Grain
Active Health
BREAD
For Digestive Health
• Good Source of Calcium, B Vitamins & Iron • No Trans Fat
• Excellent Source of Fiber • No High Fructose Corn Syrup
• No Artificial Preservatives • Prebiotic Fiber • Reduced Sodium
Prebiotic
NET WT 24 OZ (1 LB 8 OZ) 680g
REDEEM POINTS FOR OROWEAT TEAM USA

DAGOBA image text:
DAGOBA
ORGANIC CHOCOLATE
mon cherri
chocolate, berries & vanilla
Cacao content: 73%
DAGOBA
ORGANIC CHOCOLATE
chai
milk chocolate, crystallized ginger and spices
Cacao content: 37%
Net. Wt. 2 Oz. 56.7 g

and outside the United States that impacted the flavor industry. Committees including Flavor Labeling; Alcohol Tax and Trade; Communications and Membership; Education and Training; Finance; Joint Occupational Safety, Health and Environment; Safety Evaluation; Program; and Science continued with the help of industry volunteers and FEMA staff to address existing and emerging topics of concern.

FEMA offered members additional information and guidance through a robust series of workshops on issues ranging from flavor labeling to allergens in food to intellectual property protection to hazard communications and respiratory health and safety.

In 2009, FEMA members celebrate more than a centennial as an association. Notes FEMA Executive Director Glenn Roberts, "I know I speak for all our members when I say that we salute FEMA's eight founding member companies for their foresight. We thank the many industry volunteers who through the decades ensured that industry issues were raised and resolved with the best interests of consumer safety at heart."

Today, FEMA members benefit from scientific leadership that has formed the foundation of global safety evaluation for flavors. They appreciate an industry that values innovation in developing new ingredients — and FEMA for helping to protect trade secrets. Finally, they understand the value of FEMA membership that brings information, support and advocacy to an industry of great taste.

2000 PRICES

Sugar: 44 cents / pound **Butter**: $2.43 / pound

Eggs: 96 cents / dozen **Hershey's milk chocolate bar**: 80 cents / 1.55-ounce bar (2003)

Major Accomplishments During Our First 100 Years

1. **Tradition and Relevance:** Since its founding in 1909, FEMA has been committed to safe and high-quality flavors. FEMA has fostered a cooperative and collegial atmosphere for members in a very competitive industry as they work together on important scientific and regulatory issues. One hundred years later, FEMA maintains a vibrant, growing, member-focused organization that faces its next century with confidence and optimism.

2. **Unparalleled Science:** The FEMA Expert Panel and the preeminent FEMA GRAS program assure the safety of flavors under their conditions of intended use. The Food and Drug Administration has accepted GRAS determinations for more than 40 years.

3. **Alcohol Action:** During Prohibition, FEMA supported federal legislation allowing the sale of flavors and extracts that were "unfit for beverage use," and helped the federal government establish the "drawback" mechanism. Flavor manufacturers were required to pay a federal alcohol tax of only $1 per proof gallon — a levy that has not changed in nearly 80 years.

4. **Global Reach:** The safety assessment principles of the FEMA Expert Panel have been embraced around the world, resulting in more than 1,500 FEMA GRAS flavoring substances accepted by the Joint FAO/WHO Expert Committee on Food Additives (JECFA) as candidates for a global open positive list.

5. **Vanilla Standard:** FEMA offered defining input to the FDA in support of the FDA's standard for vanilla extract and other vanilla flavorings. This is the FDA's only standard of identity for a flavoring extract.

6. **Workplace Safety:** FEMA has supported flavor manufacturers in their efforts to have the safest workplaces possible. Included are significant tools to assist member company compliance with federal standards. Our initiatives are supported by 10 years of education on respiratory health and safety issues.

7. **Intellectual Property Protection:** Consistent with a long history of protecting trade secrets of members, FEMA secured amendments to the New Jersey Right to Know law, ensuring the return of more than 50,000 proprietary flavor formulas. FEMA garnered additional protection for trade secret flavor formulas in the federal bioterrorism legislation passed after the Sept. 11 tragedy.

8. **Leveraged Expertise:** Forty years ago, FEMA supported the founding of the International Organization of the Flavor Industry (IOFI), and has led the effort to "internationalize" the FEMA scientific program through global financial support and management under IOFI.

9. **Anticipation:** Throughout its history, FEMA has monitored industry and regulatory developments and created strategies to address upcoming events, consistent with the association's mission to both promote the business interests of members and protect consumers.

10. **Membership Value:** Whether interpreting regulations from the United States and abroad or maintaining a massive repository of information on federal and state regulations, FEMA has provided valuable counsel and support to its members. Through workshops, symposia, publications, its Web site and staff consultations, FEMA has kept members up-to-date on topics that affect their businesses now and into the future.

Chapter 12

Forum on the Future

Members of the FEMA Board of Governors 2008-09 are (first row, left to right): Joanne Ferrara (president elect), Howard Smith Jr. (president), Hamed Faridi, Ray Hughes (vice president and secretary) and Glenn Roberts (executive director); (second row, left to right): Thomas Buco, Leslie Blau, Robert Pellegrino, Christopher Gibson, Arthur Schick (treasurer) and Mark Scott; (third row, left to right): John Hallagan (general counsel), Richard Pisano Jr., Ed Hays, George Robinson and Kevin Renskers.

hroughout the history of the association, FEMA members have always anticipated industry and market trends and developed plans to address them. At the 99th annual FEMA meeting in May 2008 in Hilton Head, S.C., FEMA held a special session to talk about the future. As a coda to the history of FEMA's first century, the following are highlights of this free-ranging discussion.

With regard to global regulatory issues, two major topics were covered. One was the future of GRAS, with a focus on its viability, acceptability and relevance. "Our intent would be to strengthen a program that already creates value for FEMA members and for U.S. regulators, and to provide reassurance to our critics," commented Bill Troy of Firmenich, Inc.

Bill Troy

Ken Schrankel, chair of both the FEMA Safety Evaluation Coordination Committee and the International Organization of the Flavor Industry Science Board, discussed the possibility of expanding membership in the FEMA Expert Panel (FEXPAN) to broaden its geographic reach and to include outside observers.

The continued evolution of FEXPAN to embrace an even broader panel of experts will help FEMA science expand further on the international stage. This in turn will have a positive impact on domestic U.S. challenges: "If we continue to broaden the global acceptance of FEMA's excellent science, it will come back as an even more powerful tool to help us address the issues we face here in the U.S.," commented former

Chuck Manley

FEMA President Chuck Manley.

The second topic, European regulatory developments, could change the face of the global industry significantly. Troy gave a recent example — and a warning: The exclusion of 347 flavor materials from the European positive list that have already "received appropriate qualifying review" in the United States will result in "hundreds if not thousands of reformulations" if this situation is not addressed.

Emerging regulatory challenges will extend to all parts of the globe. FEMA Executive Director Glenn Roberts noted, "We have REACH, which is going to have a broad impact not just on the fragrance side but on the flavor side — and not just in Europe, but around the world. We also have to deal with a global regulatory database."

Session participants advocated an aggressive FEMA global outreach program and political advocacy beyond the United States in order to promote better understanding and usage of FEMA's approach to safety assessment. Added Roberts, "We have to get WHO/FAO Codex Alimentarius standards adopted in every country around the world." An increasingly strong partnership between FEMA and IOFI, along with horizontally and vertically integrated advocacy efforts within companies and within the industry, were also seen as essential.

In a Science and Technology presentation, Chuck Manley predicted that changes in biochemistry and physiology "will establish some very new scientific principles for the industry and for FEMA." Included are developments in studies of the olfactory system and how the sense of taste travels to and through the brain.

New methods in screening will also evolve. Noted Manley, "High throughput screening of new flavor ingredients is going to play a role in identifying substances that trigger taste or olfactory receptors."

Trends in flavor screening will have other, wider applications — in developing new taste-aroma compounds, in toxicological testing, and in identifying contaminants in flavors.

Workplace safety, genotoxicity and naturals will continue to challenge industry science and technology.

Hamed Faridi of McCormick & Company noted how information technology has "revolutionized all aspects of the business...helping companies manage the global supply chain and operate efficiently around the globe." According to Faridi, "IT benefits now and into the future

Hamed Faridi

include e-marketing, managing the customer relationship, finding new suppliers, helping reduce time and cost of business-to-business transactions, helping to increase trade between distant geographies, managing orders and payments, and much more." He added, "R&D of the future would be heavily system-based and rely less on people."

Session participants suggested that the industry should optimize the use of IT; one example is knowledge management. Leslie Blau of Firmenich, Inc. noted that flavor chemistry is a "memory game"; creative uses of IT can help to organize basic information across the industry, allowing flavorists within companies to apply more time to the artistry aspects of flavors. The industry of the future could have shared compounding resources using robotics or other technical systems, thus cutting costs and increasing value based on unique intellectual property within product development at each company.

Representatives from FEMA member companies and FEMA staff participated in discussions that yielded an informative Futures Forum session at the 99th annual meeting in May 2008. The participants were:

Technical Systems
Hamed Faridi – McCormick & Company
Cynthia Astrack - Astral Extracts Ltd.
Leslie Blau – Firmenich, Inc.
Tim Webster - David Michael & Co., Inc.
Sean Taylor – The Roberts Group/FEMA

Science and Technology
Chuck Manley - Retired [Takasago International Corporation (USA)], incoming FEMA senior science adviser
Tim Adams - The Roberts Group/FEMA
Tom Buco - Mastertaste
Debbie Nickels – International Flavors & Fragrances Inc.
Fred Stults - Givaudan

Culinary Trends
Joanne Ferrara – ConAgra Foods
George Robinson – Ottens Flavors
Ellen Gardner - The Roberts Group/FEMA

Global Regulatory
Bill Troy – Firmenich, Inc.
Kathleen Crossman - Givaudan
Lorna Hopkinson - International Flavors & Fragrances Inc.
Kevin Renskers – Takasago International Corporation (USA)
Ken Schrankel - International Flavors & Fragrances Inc.
John Cox - The Roberts Group/FEMA

Economy and the Political Environment
Glenn Roberts - The Roberts Group/FEMA
Kip Gibson - International Flavors & Fragrances Inc.
Bob Pellegrino - Givaudan
Richard Pisano Sr. - Citrus and Allied Essences Ltd.
Mark Scott - T. Hasegawa USA

The Environment
Howard Smith Jr. - Virginia Dare Extract Co., Inc.
Bob Leggett - Retired (PepsiCo)
Richard Pisano Jr. - Citrus and Allied Essences Ltd.
Skip Rosskam - David Michael & Co., Inc.
Cathy Cook - The Roberts Group/FEMA

Supplier and the Customer
Art Schick - PepsiCo
William Downey - Retired (Fritsche/Givaudan)
James Heinz – Bell Flavors & Fragrances, Inc.
Bob Weeks - *Food Product Design*/Virgo Publishing
Wayne Wheeler – W & g Flavors Incorporated
Christie Gavin - The Roberts Group/FEMA

Consumer Trends
Ed Hays – The Coca-Cola Company
Peter Lombardo – Robertet, Inc.
Colin Ringleib - PepsiCo
Ellen Gardner - The Roberts Group/FEMA

Joanne Ferrara

Joanne Ferrara of ConAgra Foods addressed culinary trends, commenting, "The American palate is changing...due to the diversity of travel." Demographics play a role as well: "Young people today are much more receptive to tasting new and different things," added Ferrara.

Consumer companies are increasingly focused on innovation in product development; Ferrara observed, "Many of our companies now have chefs to help bring new and innovative ideas to our food palates...and the array of spices... are becoming more and more creative in the design of food products." A growing trend is "sweet heat" — the combination of savory with sweet, like the use of chili peppers in chocolate and ice cream. Consumer interest in transparency will create labeling and intellectual property protection challenges.

Ed Hays of The Coca-Cola Company reviewed consumer trends. Among them are the need to preserve local identity in the face of the developing "global culture" and time management in an age of time scarcity.

Increasingly, Hays observed, consumers "want escapism to cushion them from realities of a cold, harsh, rapidly changing world." One way is to "make something from scratch." This may create opportunities both in developing and packaging flavors with pre-portioned foods to satisfy time-starved consumers.

Hays noted consumers will desire "a personal sanctuary where they can retreat and get away by fortifying the body with supplements, foods and beverages to starve/stave away disease."

FEMA Executive Director Glenn Roberts addressed political and economic trends. "The food safety bill currently before Congress has some GRAS provisions," noted Roberts. This may create a need for ongoing action from FEMA.

Ed Hays

If the economy fails to improve, "FEMA's going to get pressure from members to cut costs, avoid dues increases for more years, spend down the reserve. We will have fewer volunteers precisely at the moment when our strategic plan calls for expanding the pool of volunteers," said Roberts.

In a presentation on the environment, Howard Smith Jr. of Virginia Dare Extract Co., Inc. noted concern about the environment was at an all-time high and was becoming a mainstream issue. He covered

Glenn Roberts

trends including global warming, going green, carbon footprints, social responsibility, ethical sourcing, food miles, organic, and fair trade.

Stated Smith in his opening comments, "Many believe sustainable development will be the issue for the 21st century. Others are concerned that consumers will become confused by all the claims being made and grow tired or become disillusioned."

The group agreed that the flavor industry had a strong environmental story to tell, with sustainable products like essential oils, ethical sourcing of raw materials from developing countries, and the concerted effort by industry companies to promote sustainability as opportunities to address this growing concern.

Art Schick of PepsiCo presented trends on customer supplier relationships. "The industry will be challenged to develop and deliver more targeted, better-for-you products," said Schick. He added, "Because consumers want natural and authentic when they look at health and wellness, there may be a great opportunity to use flavor to mask better-for-you ingredients like fish oil."

Howard Smith Jr.

Speed to market will be important and will have an impact on resource allocation and account management. In a world of highly segmented products, companies will be challenged to assure supply.

Art Schick

The trend toward core supplier lists may give way to suppliers "based on best of breed capability," noted Schick. "Maybe some companies are great in the savory area and some in the sweet."

The industry may also see more joint development between consumer product and flavor companies and shared-risk-and-return types of pricing.

Schick concluded: "In the past, the customer had power. Now the power equation is shifting, particularly as industries consolidate. There is more balance than in the past between customers and suppliers."

If you'd like to read more about the issues discussed at the Futures Forum session, please go to www.femaflavor.org.

155

The Development of Instrumental Methods of Analysis and Their Impact on the Flavor Industry

R.L. Hall, J. Walradt, P.G. Hoffman

No factor in the past century has had a greater impact on the flavor industry than the development of instrumental methods of analysis. It is equally true that no industries have been more strongly affected by this development than the flavor and fragrance industries.

Where we were in 1945

A major aspect of chemistry since — and even before — its evolution from alchemy has been the task of separating (isolating) individual constituents, preferably single chemical substances, from mixtures. In the flavor industry, these mixtures often were the essential oils or extracts of a natural source such as a spice, a fruit or a botanical. The body of techniques for separating and identifying the individual constituents by the methods available before 1945 is now called "wet chemistry."

156

The traditional — wet chemistry — tools for isolation were few in number, laborious and frequently ineffective. The principal tools were fractional distillation, crystallization, column chromatography, solvent extraction, and partition between two solvents.

The means of identification of the separated — and hopefully single — substance usually involved chemical modification, derivatization or degradation, as by hydrolysis or oxidation, into more easily identifiable compounds. Tests for functional groups were important, e.g., the Schiff test for aldehydes and the Beilstein test for halides. Other tests for functional groups were more explicitly chemical, such as reaction with hydroxylamine to produce an oxime indicating an aldehyde or a ketone. Ultraviolet spectra could be obtained but were of limited use in determining specific chemical structure.

A key observation was the melting point of a substance or its solid derivative; there were tables of melting points of compounds. For final proof of identity with a suspected compound, one mixed together a small amount of each and measured the melting point of the mixture. If the "mixed melting point" was not depressed below the melting point of the known compound, it fairly conclusively proved identity.

Elemental analysis for the carbon, hydrogen and oxygen content was also an important tool. Physical property tests such as density and optical rotation were often helpful in confirming identity. Finally, and most important for the flavor industry, were the taste and odor — the flavor characteristics — of both the natural mixture and its constituents. They guided the application of the chemical methods, in spite of their limitations.

The limitations of these methods were severe indeed. One needed enough material to handle physically; it was difficult if not impossible to work with less than a few milligrams. The isolation methods were crude and insensitive, so major portions of a natural product such as an essential oil remained an unresolvable mixture of unknown composition. The consequence was that in the definitive work of the time, Ernst Guenther's "The Essential Oils" (D. Van Nostrand & Company, 1948), only a few constituents of any essential oil were known (as shown in the table on page 162).

Because the analytical methods were so cumbersome, insensitive and undiscriminating, adulteration of the more expensive products was widespread and its detection difficult or, more often, impossible. Identification of the minor constituents of a natural flavor source was usually impossible; trace constituents, including many now known for their defining contributions to characterizing flavors, were wholly unknown. Safety testing was often done on the entire natural product because such a large proportion of its constituents remained unknown. Inevitably this raised the question of whether those test results would apply to the same oil from different sources or other years.

Flavor chemists of the time were trained in the apprenticeship tradition, often by European mentors. Many had a background in relevant science, but some did not. Important in their training was achieving familiarity with the odors (flavors) of a large number of raw materials, each from multiple sources. In attempting to judge the quality of a raw material or to match an existing flavor, flavor chemists found that the nose was the ultimate tool, then as now.

In the pre-instrumental era, the means to apply that tool were few and simple. Most important was the blotter strip, dipped into the product to be examined. The more volatile constituents evaporated and could be smelled first, followed by the less volatile ones. A flavor to be matched and the attempted match were examined side-by-side, with the missing flavor notes marked for addition and the inappropriate ones for elimination.

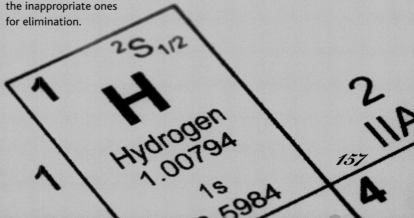

Flavor formulation was therefore far more difficult than today, and far more an art than a science. In fact, the contrast with today could hardly be greater:

In 1913, J.J. Thomson discovered that a stream of ionized neon passing through magnetic and electric fields was separated into two isotopes of different mass.

Chemists now routinely work with nanogram quantities — ppb, ppt — and as discussed later, the number of constituents so far identified has increased by more than an order of magnitude. Though the blotter strip has not disappeared, it serves as only a supplement to more sophisticated methods.

The development of instrumental methods

None of the new instrumental methods appeared fully developed, and all at once. Each had antecedents and a period of development that continues today.

Spectroscopy began with Herschel's observation that light passing through a prism heated an area beyond the visible red more than any part of the visible spectrum. Chromatography began in 1903 with Tswett using a chalk column to separate plant pigments. In 1941 Martin and Synge published their work on liquid-liquid chromatography, which ushered in the current era of the different chromatographic techniques. Mass

spectrometry began with Goldstein's discovery in 1886 of "canal rays," and the later discovery by J.J. Thomson that the particles making up these "rays" were not all of the same mass. Quite probably the first commercial method of instrumental analysis was Arnold Beckman's pH meter, which began development in 1934. The Beckman DU UV-vis spectrophotometer, another milestone instrument, followed closely in 1941.

Gas chromatography (GC) was first suggested by Martin and Synge in their 1941 paper and later developed by Martin and James in 1951-1952. GC was quickly recognized by the flavor industry as a tool with immediate application for the separation of flavor volatiles. Also recognized early was the potential for sniffing eluted peaks to pinpoint important odor compounds. Of all the instrumental methods, gas chromatography has had the greatest impact on the flavor industry.

The GC technique consists of injecting a small amount of gas, or a liquid that can be vaporized, at the head of a heated column. A nonreactive gas, usually helium or hydrogen, is used to carry the mixture through the tube. Separations occur based on differences in boiling points and partition ratios between the stationary phase and the moving gas phase. In the 1950s and 1960s those columns were 1/8- to 1/4-inch in diameter, four to six feet long and packed with various media such as nonvolatile liquids coated on diatomaceous earth particles.

Today, open tubular (capillary) columns are made of fused silica, from 0.1 mm to 0.5 mm internal diameter and 10 to 100 meters long with very stable bonded liquid phases. The size of the sample required for the earlier packed columns was 1 to 10 micrograms, and the number of theoretical plates generated (a measure of separating efficiency) was in the range of 1,000 to 25,000. For today's capillary columns, sample sizes have decreased a hundredfold to 10 to 100 nanograms, and the separating power has increased to multiples of 100,000 theoretical plates.

Over the years, a number of different detectors were devised to increase the sensitivity and selectivity of detecting the separated constituents as they pass out of the column. The impact of these improvements on the flavor industry has been immense, particularly when coupled with new methods such as infrared spectroscopy and mass spectrometry, which provide rapid identification of each separated component. Further coupling with computers — which can provide instrument control, mathematical analysis, automated calibration, and library searching of each compound's IR or MS spectrum against a vast library of computer-stored spectra of other compounds — has led to the explosion of detailed knowledge about the constituents of natural products, including flavors.

Preparative gas chromatography uses higher capacity GC columns, up to 40 mm in diameter and 2 meters long. The injected samples are larger, up to 1 ml, and the system can be under manual or automatic control. Preparative GC is used for purifying components for structure verification by NMR or other techniques, for making critical odor value comparisons, and in a few cases for the purification of commercially useful amounts of high-value substances.

Chiral GC, the use of stereoisomeric (optically active) GC stationary phases, can separate isomers of racemic mixtures (mixtures of two optical isomers). Often only one optical isomer is biologically active, as with vitamin C. Among flavor constituents, however, the two isomers may have different characters. For example, l-linalool is found in lavender, while d-linalool is found in coriander. L-carvone is in spearmint; d-carvone is in caraway.

Paper chromatography (PC) was conceived in 1941 when Martin and Synge invented partition chromatography as an extension of their work on countercurrent extraction using two solvents. They realized they could keep one solvent, water, fixed on a silica gel column, and pass chloroform containing the mixture of solutes through the column. In that same 1941 publication, they suggested that paper could be the absorbing medium and that the mobile phase could be a gas. This led in 1944 to paper chromatography and, as mentioned earlier, in 1952 to gas-liquid partition chromatography. One application of paper chromatography in the flavor industry was the 1960 paper by William Stahl and colleagues that permitted the detection of foreign botanical extracts then used to adulterate vanilla extract. Because it is slow, lacks automation, and is not amenable to simple quantitation, paper chromatography is rarely used anymore in the flavor industry.

Thin layer chromatography (TLC) was devised by

Schreiber in 1939, but was rediscovered by Kirchner in 1951. TLC is an extension of the principles of paper chromatography in which a slurry of silica gel or some other suspended, finely divided solid with a binder is coated on a glass plate or plastic sheet and dried. The procedures then followed are the same as for paper chromatography, but the thin layer method is both more rapid and more sensitive. TLC is useful in adulteration detection and as a quality control tool for assuring product consistency.

High performance liquid chromatography (HPLC) is also an extension of the earlier chromatographic techniques, although the conditions used are very different. In HPLC, the sample to be separated is forced at high pressure through a column tightly packed with small particles, such as silica, zirconia or a less polar carbon-silicon compound. It is quite useful for the separation of nonvolatile mixtures, or for those that might decompose or react under the conditions of gas chromatography. Because HPLC is now well-automated, and multiple detectors (including mass spectrometers) are readily available, separations are becoming increasingly fast with the use of higher pressures and smaller particle size packings. In consequence, HPLC has largely replaced paper chromatography and TLC for separation, quantitative analyses and quality control of less volatile flavor materials.

Standard HPLC methods are used to characterize natural vanilla extracts for geographical origin and vanillin content, based on the proportions of constituents. Other methods are used to determine composition of plant polyphenols, content of piperine and capsaicin heat compounds, antioxidants, anthocyanins, vitamins, sugars and artificial sweeteners, amino acids, agricultural residues and other contaminants, etc.

Infrared spectroscopy (IR) is based on the absorption of energy at different frequencies in the infrared spectrum that match the stretching and bending frequencies of the interatomic bonds in a chemical substance. This relationship was well-established in the 1930s. Because each specific bond between two atoms often has a unique absorption wavelength, IR rapidly became an effective method for determining functional groups in organic compounds.

The Beckman IR-1, introduced to measure butadiene

in making synthetic rubber as part of the war effort in 1942, was the first commercially produced instrument. However, the U.S. government restricted sales of the instrument until after the war. Perkin Elmer introduced its first IR instrument, the PE Model 12, in 1944. Both of these early instruments were single beam spectrophotometers and were quite slow, subject to thermal drift, and difficult to use. In 1950, Perkin Elmer introduced the PE Model 21, the first dual-beam IR spectrophotometer. It rapidly became a best seller and ushered in a whole new era of ease and speed of chemical identification.

The early IR instruments were simple dispersive spectrophotometers using a moving grating or salt prism to separate and scan through the wavelengths in the infrared spectral region. In the 1970s, Mickelson moving mirror interferometers allowing very rapid scanning became available. The signals of interest were separated from the detector output using fast Fourier transform (FT) processing, a mathematical means of converting the digital data from the interferogram into an absorption spectrum. One of the first successful capillary GC/FT-IR instruments (a GC interfaced to a Digilab FT-IR with a special gold-coated flow cell) was reduced to practice at International Flavors & Fragrances Inc.'s R&D center in the late 1970s. Hewlett-Packard introduced a purpose-built, miniaturized GC-IR detector in 1986.

Attenuated total reflectance (ATR) is a technique in which a liquid or solid sample is placed on a crystal of high refractive index, such as a diamond. The IR beam is passed through the crystal in a way that permits the reflectance from the sample surface to be scanned. Such improved optics and sampling accessories have increased sensitivity and discrimination as well as eliminated most sample preparation for liquids and solids. More recently, microscopes have been added with IR objectives that allow one to identify visually a microscopic target and obtain infrared spectra of it to help with chemical characterization. The FT-IR microscope is useful as an aid to identifying foreign material in ingredients and finished flavors.

Mass spectrometry (MS) began with the discovery by J.J. Thomson in 1913 that a stream of ionized neon passing through magnetic and electric fields was separated into two isotopes of different mass. The first mass spectrometers were built, separately, by Arthur Dempster and Francis Aston in 1918 and 1919. In the use of MS, the separated flavor constituents or their fragments are ionized and passed through the electric/magnetic fields of the MS; the fragments, separated by mass and charge, are measured.

Mass spectrometers were used in the 1950s to identify flavor compounds synthesized or isolated by classical techniques. In the early 1960s, numerous research groups worked on coupling the separating power of the GC with the identification power of the mass spectrometer. A good example of the progress being made at that time is found in the 1965 paper by McFadden and co-workers at the USDA Western Regional Research Laboratory, where they reported identification of 58 compounds from strawberry essence using a GC capillary column directly coupled to a fast scanning mass spectrometer.

Today there is a variety of highly sensitive MS detectors including single quadrupole, magnetic sector, ion-trap or time of flight that are useful for identification. The triple quadrupole is used for trace quantitation of targeted compounds at the picogram (one millionth of one millionth of a gram) level. HPLC coupled with MS was used by FEMA in a multi-laboratory program to determine the levels of polycyclic heterocyclic amines in process flavors. It showed that the total intake from the use of flavors was insignificant, and lower than that from the corresponding foods.

GC-MS is now the tool of first choice for separating and identifying the volatile constituents of flavors. Several hundred components can sometimes be determined in a single analysis, along with relative quantitation. When one encounters unknown components, GC-olfactometry (sniffing) can estimate the odor value; then the use of GC-IR may help to determine functional groups present or absent. To unambiguously determine an unknown structure, though, there is no substitute for the information provided by NMR. This generally involves preparative GC or LC to isolate enough material (around 1 microgram) to obtain useful spectral data.

Isotopic methods include both stable isotope ratio analysis (SIRA) and radiometric analyses or liquid scintillation (LS). Isotopes are atoms of the same element, but with different atomic weights because their nuclei contain different numbers of neutrons.

SIRA is an application of mass spectrometry. Because MS measures weights, isotopes of the same element are separated and measured separately. LS measures the naturally occurring unstable isotopes. These isotopes, naturally occurring in uniform trace amounts, are measured by their predictable decay.

Both SIRA and LS take advantage of the fact that biological and geological processes tend to favor the accumulation of one isotope over another in the reactions that produce their biological or geological end products. These isotopic methods permit differentiating one product from a specified botanical source from the chemically identical product from another botanical source, or from a geological source such as petroleum. For example, these methods can distinguish vanillin from vanilla beans from vanillin as a byproduct of the paper pulp industry or vanillin synthesized from guaiacol.

Site-specific natural isotope fractionation NMR (SNIF-NMR) also permits the differentiation of the origins of flavors. Radiometric analysis is similar to the radiocarbon dating used by archeologists and paleontologists. Interestingly, SIRA is also a spin-off from radiocarbon dating, developed as a means to refine the isotopic variations due to biosynthesis.

Researchers in the food industry realized that these isotopic methods could be used to authenticate the origin of a variety of products such as honey, maple syrup, orange juice, caffeine, etc. The flavor industry quickly applied the technologies to protect the integrity of its products. These isotopic methods proved particularly useful in detecting adulteration of flavor products. In the early 1970s when these methods were developed, tens of grams and multiple milligrams were required for radiometric and SIRA analyses, respectively. Currently, due to the advent of gas chromatography-isotope ratio mass spectrometry (GC-IRMS), preparative capillary gas chromatography (PCGC) and accelerator mass spectrometry (AMS), only a sub-milligram to a nanogram sample is required. FEMA was instrumental in the development and use of these isotopic methods in cooperation with the University of Georgia.

NMR takes advantage of the fact that some atomic nuclei possess a "spin" that, with their electric charge, creates an electric current and an associated magnetic field — in effect, a tiny electromagnet. When an external magnetic field is applied, the magnetic field of the nucleus tends to twist in line with the external field, and it precesses, or wobbles, like a top or a gyroscope. When a weak external radio wave is applied to the atom(s) in question, and the radio wave has the same frequency as the precession of the nucleus, the system resonates by picking up additional energy and then emitting it as an impulse that can be measured by an external detector. The frequency of resonance will depend on the location and environment of an atom within the molecule, and this makes the technique a valuable tool for determining molecular structure.

With the introduction of commercial instruments such as the Varian A-60 in 1961, NMR began to be applied to confirming the chemical structures of synthesized aroma chemicals and some of the most abundant constituents isolated from essential oils by classical wet chemical methods. Milligram quantities of sample were required. By the early 1970s, instrumentation was sufficiently advanced (higher field strength magnets, minicomputers, and fast Fourier transform signal processing) and sensitivity improved to the point that interpretable spectra could be obtained from multi-microgram quantities of sample isolated by GC (and even wide bore capillary GC). This level of sensitivity made NMR an indispensable technique for accurately determining unknown molecular structure and for distinguishing isomer differences.

Even with the vast improvement of instrumental methods to the present state of the art in flavor chemistry research, flavor — as perceived by human olfactory and taste senses — has not been superseded. It is not uncommon to see a flavorist with his nose close to the exit port of a GC so he can decide which components are of further interest, now aided by voice recognition software to replace handwritten notes. Flavor remains the compass, the guiding star, the final measure of value of flavors and their ingredients.

As mentioned in preceding paragraphs, the advent of the computer and its dramatic size reduction and performance improvement has been a major transforming factor. All analytical instrumentation now includes imbedded electronic control and processing power, usually augmented by connection to a "personal" computer. By recording and analyzing the data in real time, and comparing those data against libraries of previously recorded data, scientists have seen the power,

accuracy, speed and total output of all these methods of instrumental analysis increase enormously in the past 50 years. Reinforcing that increase is the availability of other auxiliary equipment, such as automatic sampling, bar code technology and sample manipulating equipment, that perform their operations far faster and more precisely and reliably than human technicians ever could.

The consequences for the flavor industry have been beyond the imaginations of those working in the field 60 years ago. One example is the expansion of knowledge about natural products constituents of interest to the industry, as shown in the table below.

Occasionally, one of the newly revealed constituents of a natural mixture raises questions of safety that must be pursued to a conclusion. Far more often, however, the numerous minor constituents turn out to be innocuous. Many times they are major constituents of some other natural product, thus removing any doubts about safety that would otherwise spring from a large fraction of unknown composition.

More detailed knowledge of composition has, with increased understanding of metabolism and toxicological data, led to far more knowledge of structure/activity relationships and more secure and economical approaches to safety evaluation. Such sensitive methods of isolation and identification have helped in the detection of pesticide residues or environmental contaminants that would otherwise go unnoticed.

Constituents Identified in Typical Essential Oils

Natural Product	Number of Constituents Identified in 1948*	Number of Constituents Identified in 2007**
Black Peppercorns	7	273
Peppermint Leaves	21	225
Orange Peel	9	207
Lemon Peel	24	194
Rosemary Leaves	6	124
Coriander Seeds	13	122
Grapefruit Peel	4	121
Lime Peel	18	120
Bergamot Peel	9	114
Spearmint Leaves	6	100

*Guenther, E., "The Essential Oils" (6 vols.), D. Van Nostrand & Co., 1948
**Nijssen, B., van Ingen-Visscher, K., and Donders, J. "Volatile Compounds in Food 9.1," Centraal Instituut voor Voodingsonderzioek TNO. Zeist, The Netherlands 2007. www.vcf-online.nl/VcfHome.cfm

In virtually all cases, the detection limits of the most sensitive methods are far below the levels at which the residues or contaminants could exert any adverse effects on humans, animals or the environment.

Other consequences of the instrumental revolution include improved quality control of natural sources, vastly improved formulation of synthetic flavors, and the ability to "reverse engineer" complex natural mixtures and competitive products. A major advance is the effective detection of adulteration, including natural vs. synthetic origin and the substitution of less expensive raw materials for the expected ingredients. Detection of even crude adulteration often was far beyond the reach of the wet chemistry methods. Today, proof of species and geographical area of origin is routinely done on a few milligrams or a single seed.

Doubtless we will continue to probe further down the quantitative scale and discover new constituents of natural sources that play an important role in flavor, as evidenced by the recent discovery of rotundone as the source of the distinctive aroma of black pepper. Efforts are also under way to develop sensors (detectors) for use with gas chromatographs that can be programmed to respond to specific odors in the same manner as the human nose. But each sensor has to be "taught" by the human nose, and that nose is still the most sensitive — and the only relevant — determinant.

The authors wish to acknowledge very helpful comments and suggestions from Klaus Bauer, Jeffrey Bloch, James Broderick, Roman Grypa, Charles Manley and Michael Zapf.

Company Histories

As FEMA proudly celebrates its 100th anniversary, it is important to note that many of our member companies can trace their roots back more than a century. In fact, some have been in business for many generations prior to the formation of our national association.

Our membership today is diverse. Many companies are still family owned. Others grew from mergers and acquisitions during the past several decades. We have domestic-focused enterprises and large multinationals. FEMA members also include consumer products companies that formulate some of their own flavors. We have ingredient manufacturers, importers and compounders, all demonstrating an appreciation of the function and benefit of flavors.

The heritage of our industry is a wonderful blend of American, German, Dutch, Swiss, Japanese, French and many other cultures. While there are distinct differences in these cultures, there has always been one very strong unifying thread in our history: Our companies were founded with a strong entrepreneurial spirit. It is this spirit, along with the pursuit of scientific breakthroughs and a flair for creativity, that has helped our industry grow and has sustained us through the years.

As you have read, we have been confronted with challenges in each of our 10 decades. It speaks to the strength and character of FEMA and its members that the association has been able to find consensus to navigate successfully through whatever challenges we have faced.

The short summaries in this section are just a taste of the rich heritage that our member companies bring to FEMA. I'd like to thank the many member companies that contributed historical perspective to this section, and to other parts of the book.

Skip Rosskam
Co-Chair, FEMA 100th Anniversary
Book Committee
President, David Michael & Co., Inc.

FEMA members at the 1930 annual meeting in Washington, D.C.

As part of its anniversary year celebration, FEMA is showcasing more in-depth company histories on its Web site. Go to www. femaflavor.org for more details.

A.M. Todd Company
Kalamazoo, Michigan • Founded: 1869

In 1869, 19-year-old Albert May Todd started his own peppermint oil business on a small Michigan farm. It soon became the A.M. Todd Company, the largest mint processor in the world, with Albert Todd becoming recognized as the "Peppermint King." Based on his chemistry studies, Albert Todd introduced innovations that improved peppermint oil — introduction of a heartier, winter-resistant Black Mitcham, better processing equipment, new distillation methods and new authenticity testing.

In 1910 the company introduced the first Scotch spearmint into commercial production and in the 1960s successfully pioneered the development of the disease-resistant irradiated peppermint varieties generally planted today. Todd led the significant expansion of mint cultivation in Oregon, Idaho and Northern California in the 1980s and '90s. Further expansion continued through a venture onto the Indian subcontinent in 1997, which is now India's largest contract agriculture program.

Today the A.M. Todd Company has a broad range of competencies offering a full line of products that support the strategic brands of customers, including citrus oils, certified organic flavors, colors and isolates, special-effect ingredients, and therapeutic botanical ingredients, in addition to high-quality mint oils. With facilities in the United States, India, Europe, South America, Mexico and China, the fourth generation of the family is guiding a fully global Todd organization into the 21st century.

Agilex Flavors & Fragrances, Inc.
Rancho Santa Margarita, California • Founded: 2006

An amalgam of the company's supporting signature, "Agility. Passion. Excellence," Agilex was formed in 2006, with roots dating back almost 20 years earlier to the establishment of AromaTech in Somerville, N.J. AromaTech was one of six flavor and fragrance companies

Flavor Division President Tom Damiano

acquired by Flavor and Fragrance Group Industries (FFG) between 1999 and 2006 that ultimately became Agilex.

In addition to AromaTech, FFG acquired International Fragrance & Technology (IFT) of Canton, Ohio; Key Essentials (KEI), Rancho Santa Margarita, Calif.; Flavor Source, Anaheim, Calif.; Technology Flavors & Fragrances (TFF), Amityville, N.Y.; and Western Flavors & Fragrances, Livermore, Calif.

Combining "big-company resources and small-company values," Agilex is one of the few concept-to-completion suppliers able to provide both flavors and fragrances to a wide variety of industries. Today it provides flavors for beverages, hard and soft confections, baked goods, tobacco, dairy, pharmaceutical and nutraceutical products, and fat-free, reduced-fat, and sugarless products.

Allured Business Media
Carol Stream, Illinois • Founded: 1921

When Earl Allured launched a confectionery industry magazine from his offices in the Chicago Stock Exchange building in 1921, it was the beginning of a family publishing dynasty. Earl's son, Stanley Allured, joined the business in 1949 and went on to assume management of *The American Perfumer*, which was originally founded in 1906 by Ungerer & Co. Over several decades, *The American Perfumer* evolved into *Perfumer & Flavorist* magazine.

In the magazine's early days, its news section was regularly filled with birth, marriage, travel and death announcements because industry members knew each other but rarely met face to face. Stanley Allured also traveled extensively during his 40-plus years of covering the flavor and fragrance industry worldwide. He began attending perfumery and flavor chemists' meetings in 1960, and eventually was made an honorary member of the groups.

Stanley Allured

Through the years, Stanley Allured was joined by other family members in the business, including his wife, Betty Lou, and their three daughters, Nancy, Jean and Janet, along with several grandchildren. Today, Stanley Allured's grandson Jeb Gleason-Allured serves as editor of *Perfumer & Flavorist*.

From left: Jeb Gleason-Allured (*Perfumer & Flavorist* magazine), Alissa Leegwater (coffee evaluations specialist) and Glenn Mangarelli (flavorist) sit in on a coffee flavor tasting panel.

Astral Extracts Ltd. (ASTRAL)
Syosset, New York • Founded: 1978

A family-owned business, Astral Extracts was founded by Alexander Astrack in 1978 and is now owned wholly by Cynthia Astrack. The company is a certified Women's Business Enterprise (WBE) and manufactures a complete line of citrus oils and byproducts, citrus fractions, washed lemon oil, flavor manufacturing ingredients, specialty manufacturing ingredients, essential oils and aroma chemicals including maltol, ethyl maltol and natural maltol.

After World War II, Alexander Astrack, a decorated veteran who served under Gen. George Patton, formed the Alexander Astrack Company to offer consulting services to the food industry. During this time, he persuaded the industry to change from extracting dried fruits to working with fruit juice concentrates; he also was instrumental in introducing America to disodium inosinate, disodium guanylate, monosodium glutamate and fish extracts made in Japan.

During the 1960s, Astrack expanded into supplying essential oils, fruit juice and citrus concentrates, and byproducts. In the 1970s, the company sought basic ingredients from both domestic and international entities, acting as importers, distributors, agents and manufacturers of specialty ingredients. After ASTRAL was formed in the late '70s, the company became a primary source for basic manufacturing ingredients.

Cynthia Astrack joined ASTRAL in 1991, leading the company in developing strategic partnerships with producers around the world. To accommodate the growing changes in flavor development, ASTRAL and its partners developed key ingredients, including citrus fractions, nootkatone, decanal, aroma chemicals, mustard oil, organically certified concentrates and ingredients.

Alexander Astrack being awarded Ministry of Finance Medal by Mr. Nozaki, finance minister of Japan in 1965

Cynthia Astrack, Mr. Wang ShaoHai, chairman and GM of BTC, and Ms. Jing Chen at BTC facility in China in 2001

Aust & Hachmann (Canada) Ltd
Montreal, Quebec, Canada • Founded: 1991

In 1991, Hamburg, Germany-based Aust & Hachmann knew the worldwide vanilla market was changing. A nearly 25-year-old quota system for vanilla beans from Madagascar and the Comoros — almost 80 percent of the world's vanilla trade — was finally abandoned, and from this new open market Aust & Hachmann (Canada) was born. The German parent company drew on its 100-plus years of experience in the vanilla trade to offer the North American marketplace a new and alternative source for natural vanilla beans and vanilla byproducts.

With regional partnerships in Madagascar, Uganda, Papua New Guinea and French Polynesia, Aust & Hachmann (Canada) can keep its fingers on the pulse of the global vanilla trade. The company offers vanilla as a raw material (extraction grade vanilla beans, industrial vanilla extracts, vanilla powders and vanilla sugars) and as a finished product (gourmet vanilla beans, vanilla extracts, powders and sugars). Aust & Hachmann (Canada) is also the world's largest producer of gourmet vanilla beans in glass tubes for the retail trade.

Bedoukian Research, Inc.
Danbury, Connecticut • Founded: 1972

The founder of Bedoukian Research, Dr. Paul Z. Bedoukian, was a man of many talents and interests: an organic chemist, a university instructor, a member of several industry societies, and an avid numismatist who became the world's foremost authority on Armenian coinage.

His commercial prominence in the flavor industry started in 1960 when he developed a synthetic route to cis-3-hexenol (leaf alcohol) and began to manufacture it. Bedoukian worked for 25 years as technical director, perfumer and consultant for many

companies including Compagnie Parento, Faberge, and International Flavors & Fragrances Inc. In 1967 he published "Perfumery Synthetics & Isolates," described as one of the top 100 scientific/technical books written that year, and in 1972 he founded Bedoukian Research to fill a niche as a supplier of high-quality specialty aroma and flavor ingredients.

Throughout his lifetime, Bedoukian was renowned as an international authority in the field of perfume and flavor materials, with 50 consecutive Annual Review articles to his credit. He was also an honorary member of the Society of Flavor Chemists. After his death in 2001, Bedoukian was posthumously given a Lifetime Achievement Award from the Fragrance Materials Association of the United States.

Paul Bedoukian's son, Dr. Robert Bedoukian, joined the company in 1975. Under his leadership, Bedoukian Research has enhanced its reputation in the flavor and fragrance and insect pheromone industries for superior quality, customer service and technical expertise.

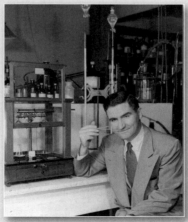
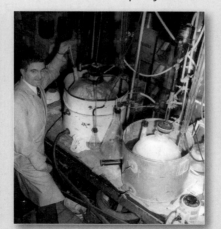

Dr. Paul Z. Bedoukian at his lab at Compagnie Parento before forming his own company

Bell Flavors & Fragrances, Inc.
Northbrook, Illinois • Founded: 1912

Edward N. Heinz and attendees at a National Confectioners Association meeting in 1976

Bell Flavors & Fragrances was founded in 1912, and its original name was the William M. Bell Company. It was founded by William M. Bell in Chicago, Ill., and his location proved to be ideal, as Chicago quickly became the "Candy Capital of the World."

In 1967 the company received a renewed spirit when Edward N. Heinz decided to take his 25 years of experience from working at Food Materials in technical sales and purchase the William M. Bell Company. Edward N. Heinz served as the president of FEMA from 1958-60.

The business was carried on with his spirit by his three sons Raymond, James and Edward, after his passing in 1987. Today Bell is one of the largest privately held flavor and fragrance companies in this competitive market.

Bell's growth can be attributed to acquiring some of the most historic flavor and fragrance houses in the world and a mission statement to provide quality products with quality service. The Schimmel & Company was one of these prize acquisitions. The Schimmel & Company historic library has over 35,000 volumes of books on flavors, fragrances, extracts, botanicals and aroma chemicals.

James H. Heinz, president of Bell, served as president of FEMA in 1995-96. Today, Jim is still an advocate and supporter of FEMA initiatives. Raymond Heinz, president of Bell GMBH, supports FEMA initiatives abroad from Bell's operations in Europe, the Middle East and Africa.

Left to right: James H. Heinz, Barbara Byrd Keenan, and Raymond J. Heinz at the entrance of Bell Germany in 2006

171

Berjé, Incorporated
Bloomfield, New Jersey • Founded: 1952

J. L. "Les" Bleimann

Alexander Bleimann

Berjé was founded in Manhattan by Julius "Les" Bleimann and Alexander Bleimann, the father and uncle of current CEO Kim Bleimann.

While Alexander worked in perfumery, Les set about developing many strategic alliances, providing access to unique byproducts and raw materials that were the foundation of the company's early growth.

Kim Bleimann joined Berjé in 1973 at its second location in Long Island City, N.Y., gaining vast industry knowledge from sharing that single office with his dad and uncle.

As Berjé outgrew its Long Island City site, it moved into its current central New Jersey location in 1981, quadrupling the company's size. The facility measures more than 180,000 square feet with what may be one of the largest raw material repositories in the United States.

Berjé's recent acquisition of the Whole Herb Company in Sonoma, Calif., is yet another step in diversification, adding a new chapter to Berjé's expanding story and positioning the firm in the sale of herbs, spices, botanicals and nutraceuticals.

Berjé's facility at 356 West Broadway in New York City in the late 1950s

Les Bleimann

Citromax Flavors
Carlstadt, New Jersey • Founded: early 1960s (as Citroil Enterprises)

Citromax was founded as Citroil Enterprises in Bloomfield, N.J., by Lee Herrera, who was later killed in a helicopter crash. Jacob Glueck, the father of current president Vivian Glueck, then took over the company and led its early production of liquid flavors, extracts and emulsions. In 1968 the company moved to a new facility in Carlstadt and began to work in the essential oil industry.

During this time, Jacob Glueck often traveled to Argentina, where he founded and established Fritzsche Brothers Argentina, a spin-off of Fritzsche, Dodge & Olcott. Now called Fritzsche SAICA, it is the only remaining company in the world with the Fritzsche name.

During the 1960s and 1970s, Jacob Glueck was one of the first to see the potential of lemons grown and processed in Argentina. He helped to introduce Argentine lemon oil to the American market, eventually founding his own growing and processing facility, called Citromax SACI,
which is today one of the largest and most modern in Argentina.

In 2003 Citroil moved into a new 40,000-square-foot manufacturing facility in Carlstadt with two laboratories, one dedicated to new flavor production and development and the other to analytical chemistry. It was designed to return the company to its roots as a flavor company alongside its essential oil business. In 2008, Citroil adopted the name of its parent company, Citromax Flavors, solidifying the relationship among the sister companies in North and South America.

173

Citrus and Allied Essences Ltd.
Belcamp, Maryland • Founded: 1933

Richard Sr. (holding the Hall award) and his three boys Christopher, Richard Jr. and Stephen

The history of Citrus and Allied Essences is intimately associated with the career of Charles Pisano, who started the company in Manhattan's Lower East Side neighborhood after working in the essential oils business for 12 years. Through contacts Pisano had made in Italy, Spain and other countries, he grew Citrus and Allied into an essential oils company serving pharmaceutical companies, confectionery manufacturers and flavor and fragrance houses. Pisano put his chemical engineering degree to good use at the company, even designing a high-vacuum glass distillation column that was displayed at the 1939 World's Fair in New York.

In 1956, Charles's son, Richard, joined the company. From the beginning he recognized the necessity of diversifying the product line, and he became well-known in the industry through his service on a number of association boards.

In the 1980s, the third generation of Pisanos — including Richard Jr., Christopher, Stephen, William and Charles Pisano — joined Citrus and Allied, fueling dramatic growth at the company. A 34,000-square-foot factory opened in Maryland in 1989 has

Charles Pisano, Richard Pisano Jr.'s grandfather

increased to 95,000 square feet today, and the company also has sales offices and warehouses in California, Illinois and Mexico. In June 2007, Richard Pisano Sr. turned over the presidency to his son Richard Pisano Jr., while Stephen Pisano assumed the role of executive vice president.

ConAgra Foods
Omaha, Nebraska • Founded: 1919 (as Nebraska Consolidated Mills)

In the heart of the prairie, four Nebraska flour mills consolidated in 1919 to form a company that would later evolve into one of North America's largest packaged food firms. Nebraska Consolidated Mills (NCM), headquartered in Grand Island, built its first new flour mill outside Nebraska in 1941, in Decatur, Ga., and then expanded beyond the continental United States with a feed, flour and corn-milling complex in Puerto Rico in 1957.

During the 1960s, NCM entered Europe with a joint venture feed mill in Spain, and by the end of the decade its flour-milling operations spanned across the United States. Reflecting its widening focus, in 1971 NCM became ConAgra Inc., with Charles M. "Mike" Harper taking the helm as the company's first chief executive officer in 1974. Through acquisitions such as Banquet Frozen Foods and Armour Foods, Harper created one of the largest food companies in the country.

With ConAgra's growth came a need for bigger facilities. In 1989 the company opened a brand new headquarters campus in Omaha. After changing its name to ConAgra Foods, Inc. in 2000, the company established a new Product Quality and Development organization and began to align and integrate the R&D assets, culminating in the consolidation of the R&D units in 2005. Today, ConAgra Foods continues its new corporate vision, first announced in 2006, with a refocused portfolio of brands and businesses designed to produce strong long-term results.

California Custom Fruits and Flavors
Irwindale, California • Founded: 1986

Terry Hall, an experienced professional in the food manufacturing industry, founded California Custom Fruits and Flavors (CCFF) in 1986. Through Terry's leadership and the dedication of employees and customers, CCFF grew and gained a reputation for superb technical ability, quality and reliability.

CCFF is distinct among the industries we serve. Our products are developed to our customers' requirements. Strong sourcing in the commodities markets and continuous investments in product development and manufacturing have propelled CCFF into additional markets, providing value to customers.

CCFF Timeline

1986 CCFF founded by Terry Hall to develop processed fruit bases and flavors.

1993 CCFF moves to its second location, a 32,000-square-foot facility in Irwindale, Calif.

1996 Celebrating its 10-year anniversary, CCFF produces over 10 million pounds of processed fruits and flavors.

1999 CCFF serves the eastern United States, Canada, Mexico and China.

2003 CCFF moves into its third building, an 85,000-square-foot facility including state-of-the-art production and on-site freezer.

2004 CCFF produces over 30 million pounds of processed fruits and flavors.

2007 Celebrating its 20th year, CCFF invests in the foodservice division.

2007 Committed to growing the flavor business, CCFF builds a flavor laboratory capable of creating flavors for beverage, dairy and bakery applications.

Consumers Flavoring Extract Company, Inc.
Brooklyn, New York • Founded: 1902

Consumers Flavoring first opened shop in the late 19th century before formally establishing itself in New York City in 1902. From the beginning, the company enjoyed success as a purveyor of seasonal novelties, essential oils and flavoring materials to the food industry, advertising in the most prestigious periodicals of the time.

Consumers remained at its original location near the present-day Tribeca neighborhood until 1950, when Kings College of Columbia University exercised its right to the land underneath the company. At the same time, Consumers needed to enlarge its facilities due to the tremendous increase in its sales to the U.S. food industry. Consumers maintained a temporary location in Brooklyn, N.Y., before moving to its current Brooklyn location with modern, state-of-the-art manufacturing facilities.

Already well-known in the United States and Canada, Consumers expanded its business internationally in the 1960s and 1970s. It achieved strong and steady growth that continues today. In 2009, the company celebrates its 107th anniversary, sharing its success with its clients, employees and friends in the food and flavor industry.

Dammann & Company, Incorporated
Oakland, New Jersey • Founded: 1935

During the decades that Frenchman Pierre Dammann was building his vanilla company in New York, Kurt Schussler — who had emigrated from Germany after World War I at age 14 — was climbing the executive ranks of the Otto Gerdau Co., a worldwide import/export firm also based in New York. Gerdau would eventually acquire Dammann, although it would be several years before Schussler, who left Gerdau in 1961 to start his own spice importing business, would reconnect with the company.

Dammann moved from its original offices on Murray Street to the Empire State Building in 1964. That same year, Schussler and Nick Gaffney purchased the assets of Dammann from Gerdau.

After temporarily residing in the World Trade Center, the company moved into its own building in Oakland, N.J., in 1986.

Throughout its nearly 75-year history, Dammann has grown into the premier supplier of vanilla beans to markets in North America, Europe and Asia. The company also sells vanilla powder, vanilla seeds, vanillin and custom chopped vanilla beans.

Most of Dammann's success has been thanks to the experience and loyalty of its employees and senior managers. Nick Gaffney has led the company for more than 45 years, Ed Raush has served as treasurer for more than 35 years, and Guy Gaffney officially took over the presidency in 2002. Dammann and its subsidiaries have formed a number of strategic partnerships with major suppliers of vanilla beans around the world, becoming the largest supplier of extract grade and gourmet vanilla beans.

Kurt Schussler visiting Uganda in 1957

Hank Kaestner inspecting vanilla vines in 2007, on one of his many trips to Madagascar

Nick Gaffney "unloading" vanilla beans from a barge that had run aground in Antalaha, Madagascar

David Michael & Co., Inc.
Philadelphia, Pennsylvania • Founded: 1896

A partnership between Atlantic City bar owner Herman Hertz and chewing gum salesman David Michael in 1896 laid the foundation for what would become David Michael & Co., Inc. Experimenting with a still in the back of Hertz's bar, the two men added a few drops of "magic ingredients" to raw corn whiskey that instantly gave it the taste of 10-year-old bourbon. They called it "Old-time Special Body & Age"®, and the original formula is still sold today. The entrepreneurs then began marketing vanilla sugar as a flavoring for ice cream, leading to Michael's Mixevan®, a blend of vanilla beans, sugar and vanillin that, when heated, produced a sweet, richly aromatic flavor. The new vanilla powder in a can gained wide acceptance as a vanilla ice cream flavor.

After Hertz died, Michael asked Eli and Robert Rosenbaum and Walter Rosskam, who had formed the R&R Chemical Company in 1919, to join his management team. The firm prospered during World War II despite sugar rationing; it tolled sugar from its clients, who then surrendered coupons to the company.

Founder David Michael died in 1935, but two sons of Rosskam and the son of Robert Rosenbaum joined the company in the years after World War II. They directed the product line's dramatic expansion into distilled spirits

David Michael, 1924

blending agents and cocktail flavors for frozen desserts. By the late 1960s, the third generation of the Rosskam and Rosenbaum families (Skip, Steve and George Rosskam and Stuart Rosenbaum) had begun to join the family business, overseeing David Michael's global expansion to Europe, Mexico and China. Now in its 113th year, the company remains true to its roots in understanding that the customer is number one.

Salesman Earl Parks, left, and Robert Rosenbaum

The BEST Vanilla Sells the MOST Ice Cream

A flavor no tongue can resist!

. . . vanilla ice-cream made with Michael's Mixevan. Mellow . . . mild . . . the taste of the genuine Mexican bean. The path of experience leads eventually to

Michael's MIXEVAN
"America's Flavorite"

There is no other vanilla flavoring to compare with this tried-and-true product. That's a strong statement, but you can prove it yourself. Read the free-trial offer on this page. Then make the test. Mixevan stands on its own merits. It needs no attorney-for-the-defense!

DAVID MICHAEL & COMPANY
Incorporated
Front and Master Sts.   Philadelphia

Make This Test at Our Expense

Place a trial order. Use all you can to give it a full, fair trial. If MICHAEL'S MIXEVAN does not produce the finest vanilla ice cream you ever tasted, return the remainder at our expense, and we will cancel the charge. Do this, by all means.

E & J Gallo Winery
Modesto, California • Founded: 1933

Ernest (left) and Julio Gallo

After years of growing and selling grapes, Ernest and Julio Gallo started their winery with $6,000 following the repeal of Prohibition. The brothers learned the craft of commercial winemaking by reading old pre-Prohibition pamphlets published by the University of California, retrieved from the Modesto Public Library basement.

Today E & J Gallo is considered one of the great American business success stories. The Gallo brothers were instrumental in creating the modern U.S. wine market. They were the first to introduce brand management and modern merchandising to the wine industry, the first in breakthrough quality initiatives such as long-term grower contracts for varietal grapes and grape research programs, and the first to establish a significant foreign sales and marketing force to export California wines overseas. Gallo has also taken the lead in developing and implementing the Code of Sustainable Wine Growing Practices, covering virtually every aspect of the wine business.

The E & J Gallo Winery is the largest family-owned winery in the world, reflected in the recent introduction of the Gallo Family Vineyards brand where second-, third- and fourth-generation family members play a major role behind the scenes.

Silesia Flavors Inc.
Hoffman Estates, Illinois • Founded: 1910

In 1910, Otto Strauhs founded Silesia in Düsseldorf, Germany, choosing "Silesia" to remember his country of birth, a former province in eastern Germany. Due to destruction during WW II and Strauhs' death, Gerhard Hanke assumed management, moving Silesia to Chemnitz, East Germany.

In 1949, Silesia returned its headquarters to Düsseldorf, where it remained until Gerd Guenther Hanke succeeded his father in 1964, increasing the scope of the company and moving all operations to the current site in Neuss, Germany. The worldwide headquarters in Neuss encompasses creation, R&D, application, production and sales/marketing.

Throughout the years Silesia has maintained a reputation as one of the foremost privately owned innovative flavor manufacturers with worldwide presence. In 1996, Silesia transferred to the fourth generation, Gerd's son Clemens Hanke. Under Clemens' guidance, Silesia continued to establish new production, creation, sales and research facilities throughout the world with emphasis on the R&D of creative, inventive flavors that are stable in modern food systems.

In 1996, the Americas headquarters, Silesia Flavors, Inc., constructed a facility for development, production and sales/marketing outside Chicago, Ill. In 1997, Silesia Flavors SEA in Singapore became development and sales/marketing headquarters for the Asian market including China (2005).

Within the past five years, Silesia International has implemented pioneering technology, researched novel flavor systems, expanded sensory evaluation, increased spray-drying capacities, automated much of its production lines, completely retrofitted state-of-the-art pilot plants and established additional sales offices on three continents.

179

Firmenich SA
Geneva, Switzerland • Founded: 1895

Firmenich is not just the name of a fragrance and flavor company. It is also the name of a family that has been personally committed to its employees and clients for over 113 years.

The company was founded by a chemist, Philippe Chuit, a businessman, Martin Naef, and — soon after — a salesman, Frederic Firmenich. By the early 1920s, the company was operating in the United States and Europe.

The head of R&D, Leopold Ruzicka, synthesized the first food flavorings and, in 1939, was awarded the Nobel Prize in Chemistry. By 1945, a dedicated Flavor Division had been created at Firmenich. This was the beginning of a dynamic phase for Firmenich Flavors and Fragrances, with accelerated growth and worldwide expansion. The result was impressive sales growth, increased production, new patent applications and office openings around the world.

Frederic Firmenich

Firmenich has always focused on robust organic growth, complemented by selective acquisitions: MCP, Intercit, Jörg Biomarin, Noville, and, most recently, the Flavor Division of Danisco, making Firmenich the second-largest flavor company in the world.

At the end of June 2008, Firmenich was the largest privately owned company in the fragrance and flavor business and No. 2 worldwide, with over 5,800 employees and annual sales of almost 3 billion Swiss francs. It is headed by a fourth-generation Firmenich, Patrick Firmenich, CEO.

Left to right: Frederic Firmenich, Philippe Chuit and Martin Naef

CEO Patrick Firmenich

Flavor Dynamics, Inc.
South Plainfield, New Jersey • Founded: 1989

Dolf De Rovira

In 1985, Dolf De Rovira formed Flavor Innovations, Inc. with a partner in Somerset, N.J., and quickly expanded into new facilities in South Plainfield, N.J.

After four years, De Rovira started Flavor Dynamics, Inc., bringing with him both the accounts he had developed and his philosophy of superb customer service and creative R&D.

FDI began in a 10,000-square-foot building in Middlesex, N.J., but in 2001 the company purchased Robertet's 27,000-square-foot building in South Plainfield, N.J., a move that put the company's R&D, sales and production all under one roof. FDI expanded further still in 2008 by acquiring the assets of California-based Progressive Flavors.

FDI President Dolf De Rovira is an active member of the flavor community, and has served as the past president of the Society of Flavor Chemists, past president of The Chemical Sources Association, a member of the board of the Flavor Heritage Society, and a member of various FEMA committees. He is the author of numerous trade publication articles, as well as the Dictionary of Flavors, a widely used sourcebook whose second edition was released in 2008. De Rovira contributes to the development of his peers by teaching courses on flavors and the culinary arts at, among others, Rutgers University, the University of Arkansas and the Culinary Institute of America.

Givaudan
Vernier, Switzerland • Founded: 1796

When young chemist Leon Givaudan, encouraged by his older brother, Xavier, established a perfumery company on the outskirts of Geneva, Switzerland, neither could have imagined the site would become the headquarters of Givaudan, a global leader of the flavor and fragrance industry.

From simple extracts to synthetic chemicals to natural flavors, Givaudan's past is marked by a stream of scientific discoveries, among them Dr. Ernest Guenther's six-volume treatise, "The Essential Oils"; a pioneering technique to extract essential oils from the byproducts of citrus processors; spray-drying of flavors to produce them in powder form; development of hydrolyzed plant protein and savory process flavors; and artificial strawberry flavor F-5662, which set the standard for strawberry flavor for many years.

Always seeking inspiration for unique flavors and taste experiences, Givaudan launched its TasteTrek program in 1999, continuing a tradition begun by Dr. Guenther in the late 1920s. Givaudan scientists travel to the ends of the Earth, using proprietary sampling techniques to capture the aroma of interesting fruits, plants, pods and herbs, which they analyze and translate into a palette of flavor inspirations.

The company itself is the result of 25 successful mergers and acquisitions over the past 213 years. Its significant flavor acquisitions include Fritzsche, Dodge & Olcott in 1990, Tastemaker in 1997, FIS in 2002, IBF in 2003, and Quest in 2007. Givaudan has grown to more than 5,000 employees worldwide, with a presence in 48 countries.

H.B. Taylor Co.
Chicago, Illinois • Founded: 1951

Horace B. Taylor

Arthur A. Levinson

H. B. Taylor sign, 1950s

Horace B. Taylor began his career as a flavor and food ingredients salesman in Chicago for James B. Long & Co. In 1951, seeking to start his own business, he approached Arthur Levinson, a Chicago area chemist and entrepreneur, who agreed to fund the H.B. Taylor Co. Eventually Taylor, Levinson and Harold Klatt formed a three-way partnership, and the company moved to its current location on South Christiana Avenue in Chicago.

H.B. Taylor Co. found significant growth in the baking industry, supplying several Midwest and Southeast bakeries with flavors, custom color blends, and sesame seeds. Thanks to Levinson's patented work with vegetable proteins, the company also developed a small business in textured soy proteins.

In 1968, H.B. Taylor was sold to National Can, which was building a food ingredient conglomerate under the National Food Ingredient Co. (NFIC) name. Taylor, Levinson, Klatt and others stayed on to play key roles in the new operation.

In the 1980s, the H.B. Taylor division was purchased by its controller, Leon Juskaitis, and a silent partner. Independent again, the company continued growing its flavor and color business by finding new markets. Under the leadership of Saul Juskaitis since his father's death in 2001, the company bought the right to manufacture and sell the former Super Industries' full line of products. More recently, it opened a 40,000-square-foot dry blend co-manufacturing facility in Elgin, Ill.

Flavor Service Pea Soup Products for the United Nations Relief and
Rehabilitation Administration, mid-1940s

183

International Flavors & Fragrances Inc.
New York City • Founded: 1958

Joseph Polak and Leopold Schwarz formed their concentrated fruit juice and flavoring compound business in Zupthen, Holland, as the 19th century closed. In 1917, A.L. van Ameringen immigrated to the United States from Holland to work for the U.S. agent of Polak & Schwarz. Soon after, he left the company and opened a 500-square-foot office in downtown Manhattan to import essential oils from Holland, a humble beginning for what would become the world's leading fragrance and flavor supplier.

In 1929 van Ameringen formed a partnership with Dr. William T. Haebler, and after acquiring an aroma chemical plant in Elizabeth, N.J., van Ameringen-Haebler, Inc. was born. Meanwhile, Polak & Schwarz opened a U.S. branch in New York in 1935. In 1958 the worldwide operations of Polak & Schwarz and van Ameringen-Haebler merged into International Flavors & Fragrances Inc., becoming a major supplier in the flavor and fragrance business and growing internationally almost overnight.

As a global powerhouse during the second half of the 20th century, IFF created many breakthroughs including: fermentation process technology, the development of key natural flavor chemical compounds, flavor modulators and flavor delivery systems. In 1968, IFF established the Monell Chemical Senses Center in conjunction with the Monell Foundation.

In 2000, IFF acquired Bush Boake Allen Inc., incorporating its 170-year history of expertise in flavors, essential oils and seasonings to create the world's largest flavor and fragrance company. In 2008, IFF had 5,300 employees in 31 countries, all focused on our shared vision to create taste and scent experiences people love.

Francis George Adair Roberts (left) and partner Arthur Boake, of A. Boake, Roberts & Co., Ltd.

Herb harvest

van Ameringen-Haebler, Inc.'s first plant in Elizabeth, N.J.

A.L. van Ameringen

Union Beach Greenhouse

J. Manheimer Inc./
Kerry Ingredients & Flavours
Clark, New Jersey • Founded: 1864 (as Leo Bernard & Co.)

In 1864, Joseph Bernard immigrated to the United States from France to start a division of Leo Bernard & Co., a business importing essential oils, perfume and soap ingredients from the company's factory in France. Twelve years later, 12-year-old Jacob Manheimer knocked on Leo Bernard's door and asked for a job. Young Manheimer learned the business well from Bernard, and in 1895, he and a partner bought the company when Bernard returned to France to retire.

Manheimer's nephews Paul and Edwin joined the team in the late 1930s, helping the business grow modestly as an importer of vanilla beans and essential oils. In 1962, after Edwin's untimely death, the business was recapitalized with Stephen, Alan and Arnold Manheimer joining Paul and Bruce Manheimer in a new corporation.

The brothers and cousins developed new sources and flavor and fragrance raw materials in China, India, South America and Indonesia.

In 1995 the company built a flavor/fragrance and USDA pilot plant in Teterboro, N.J., and in 1999 it purchased a factory in Clark, N.J.

The Manheimers decided in 2003 that further company growth would require a new paradigm and chose Kerry/Mastertaste as their buyer, closing the sale in 2004. Kerry carries on the Manheimer tradition and product lines.

MANE Flavors Inc.
U.S. Branch of V. MANE Fils
Le Bar-sur-Loup, France • Founded: 1871

MANE is a family-owned company dating back to the days when Victor Mane started producing fragrances from regional flowers and plants in Pont du Loup, France. Victor Mane built his first factory at the foot of Bar-sur-Loup village to expand their range of essential oils and extraction and to develop the production of food flavors.

Victor's sons, Eugene and Gabriel Mane, modernized and developed the business internationally between 1916 and 1958. In 1959, Maurice Mane took over for his father, Eugene. Under Maurice's leadership, the company increased its production capacity, set up research and analytical laboratories, diversified into flavorings for the food industry, and developed its international network of subsidiaries.

Maurice Mane retired in 1995 to become chairman of the Monitoring Committee, and his eldest son, Jean, was appointed president. His other son, Michel, serves as managing director for Mane's activities in the Americas and is also president of Mane USA. Jean and Michel Mane are the fourth generation in management, ensuring continuing growth and long-term strategic choices. The fifth generation is currently being trained.

Mane has created and consolidated an international network comprising more than 25 subsidiaries or representative offices and 35 agents, which provide geographical balance and coherence in more than 70 countries.

MANE Thailand

MANE Indonesia

MANE Shanghai

DET NORSKE VERITAS

SOCIAL ACCOUNTABILITY SYSTEM CERTIFICATE

Certificate No. 0183-2003-ASA-RGC-SAI

This is to certify that
the Social Accountability System
of

MANE DO BRASIL INDÚSTRIA E COMÉRCIO LTDA

at
Estrada do Guerengoê, 1421 – Curticica – Jacarepaguá – Rio de Janeiro, RJ - Brazil
Av. Indianópolis, 1460 – Bairro Planalto Paulista - São Paulo, SP - Brazil

has been found to conform to the Social Accountability Standard:

SOCIAL ACCOUNTABILITY 8000 : 2001

This Certificate is valid for the following product or service ranges:

MANUFACTURE OF FRAGRANCES AND FLAVOURS

Original Certification date:
December 11th, 2002

This Certificate is valid until:
December 11th, 2005

Place and date:
Hong Kong, February 12th, 2003

for the Accredited Unit:
Det Norske Veritas AS, Region Greater China

K. S. Cheung
Management Representative

Otavio C. da Costa
Lead Auditor

The use of the Accreditation Mark indicates accreditation in respect of the activities covered by the accreditation number 005

McCormick & Company
Baltimore, Maryland • Founded: 1889

In 1889, the 25-year-old Willoughby McCormick sold flavoring extracts and syrups door to door. Seven years later his company bought the F.G. Emmett spice business of Philadelphia, Penn., and the pieces were in place to grow a legendary business. McCormick & Company has become a global leader in the manufacturing, marketing and distribution of spices, seasonings and flavorings to the food industry.

Over the years, McCormick family members carried on Willoughby's mission. Charles P. McCormick was appointed president in 1932 when Willoughby died suddenly. He led the firm until 1969. His own son, Charles P. McCormick Jr., also led the company in the 1980s and '90s.

C.P. Sr.'s tenure was crucial as he took the reins at the outset of the Great Depression when the outlook for the business was bleak. By creating innovative human relations practices and laying the groundwork for global expansion, he put McCormick on a course for steady growth.

Since its beginnings, the company has been dedicated to ensuring quality in all its products. Innovation driven by professionals in the field of food science, sensory and culinary has positioned McCormick as the go-to company for flavor. The legend of Willoughby lives on.

Willoughby McCormick

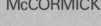

McCORMICK

Nielsen-Massey Vanillas, Incorporated
Waukegan, Illinois • Founded: 1907 (as Massey's)

Originally based in Sterling, Ill., Otis Kline and Richard Massey's company made imitation and pure vanillas and fruit flavors, and provided aromas for the cleaning industry. In 1917, they moved the firm to Webster Avenue in Chicago to be near a transportation hub.

At the same time, Chatfield Nielsen Sr. joined the company. Under the leadership of Massey and Nielsen, the company became "vanilla specialists" in 1927, offering a variety of vanilla and flavors mainly to food manufacturers.

In 1954, Nielsen purchased the company from the Massey family. His son, Chat, joined the company full time four years later. In 1963, Chat Nielsen was appointed vice president, and the company changed its name to Nielsen-Massey Vanillas. By the time Chat took over as president in the 1970s, the company had evolved into "pure vanilla specialists."

Throughout the 1990s the company launched a number of new vanilla products and opened Nielsen-Massey Vanillas International in Leeuwarden, Netherlands. Chocolate, almond, lemon, orange and coffee Pure Flavor Extracts were added to the retail and foodservice line of products in 2005-2006, a return to the company's roots. Today, the third generation of owners — Craig, Beth and Matt Nielsen — continue the legacy started by their grandfather, supplying vanilla and flavorings worldwide.

1 9 0 7 – 2 0 0 7
100 Years
NIELSEN·MASSEY VANILLAS
INCORPORATED

In 1937, the company established a curing facility in Mexico.

Ottens Flavors

Philadelphia, Pennsylvania • Founded: 1884

Henry H. Ottens

Ottens Flavors was the brainchild of Henry H. Ottens. Although he had an established career in New Jersey area real estate, Ottens recognized a business opportunity to provide flavors and colors to local food establishments. Partnering with a German chemist, he began marketing vanilla and other extracts along the East Coast, operating out of a waterfront warehouse in Philadelphia that was once used as a stopover for the Underground Railroad. Through modest growth, Ottens Flavors built a reputation as the finest local purveyor of food extracts.

In the mid 20th century, Ottens Flavors experienced true expansion in both technology and geography under the leadership of George C. Robinson, a Philadelphia banker. Three generations later, Ottens has become a flavor supplier to major food, beverage, health and wellness, and pharmaceutical companies around the world.

In 1999, Ottens Flavors boosted its capabilities by constructing a state-of-the-art facility housing new research and development labs and multi-discipline manufacturing capabilities. It has invested in a new technical facility, purchased an additional USDA location for expansion of its savory and spray drying lines, increased manufacturing capabilities with additional automation, and expanded into Mexico, South America and Asia.

With a presence on five continents, Ottens is committed on an international level to anticipating trends and serving customer needs.

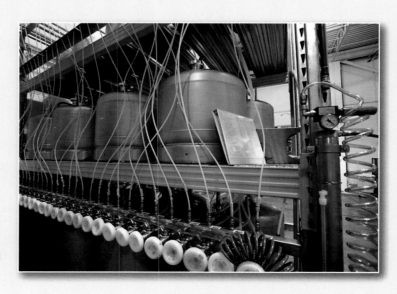

PepsiCo
Purchase, New York • Founded: 1965 (1902 as Pepsi-Cola Company)

"Brad's drink," a combination of vanilla, rare oils and a kola nut extraction named for the North Carolina pharmacist who created it, Caleb Bradham, gained new popularity when Bradham renamed it Pepsi-Cola and formed a company to market the beverage as an invigorating digestive aid. By 1911, Pepsi-Cola had bottling franchises in 24 states as it continued to expand, becoming one of the first companies in the United States to switch from horse-drawn to motor vehicles.

Pepsi-Cola made its first forays overseas during the 1930s as it registered its trademark in the Soviet Union and Latin America.

After World War II ended, the company fashioned a more sophisticated image for the soft drink, a campaign that many believe was urged on by Pepsi-Cola president Al Steele's wife, the actress Joan Crawford.

The cola drink's reign as Pepsi-Cola's only product lasted until 1964, when the company added Diet Pepsi and regional favorite Mountain Dew to its roster. In 1965, the Pepsi-Cola Company merged with salty snack maker Frito-Lay Inc. to form PepsiCo Inc. and began its expansion into a major global consumer products company. Today Pepsi-Cola's products include water, tea, coffee drinks, juices, and juice drinks, along with soft drinks.

Robertet, Inc.
Oakland, New Jersey • Founded: 1850

Since it was formed in 1850 in Grasse, France — the perfume capital of the world — Robertet has become one of the world's Top 10 suppliers of flavors and fragrances and flavor and fragrance materials. François Chauvé and his nephew, Jean-Baptiste Maubert, opened the original factory on the rue des Capucins and began extracting scents from the region's flowers and plants to supply the area's burgeoning fragrance industry.

In 1875 the business was acquired by Paul Robertet, and in 1888 it was incorporated as P. Robertet & Cie. The same year also marked the Company's first foray into the food industry, when it patented Café Instantane de Robertet — an early method for creating instant coffee.

Establishing a family tradition that has endured through four generations, Jean-Baptiste Maubert's son, Maurice, took over the business in 1923. In 1949 Robertet established its first affiliate, Robertet, Inc., to market

Maurice Maubert in 1923

the Company's raw materials in the United States. Not long after that, the Company began producing its own fragrance compounds and bases.

By 1964 it had entered the flavor business, which today accounts for 50 percent of its global sales. In 1986, Robertet acquired Jay Flavors in the United States and in 1990 renamed it Robertet Flavors, establishing a foothold in America. Robertet inaugurated a new, state-of-the-art flavor facility in Piscataway, N.J., in 1999; and in 2008 the Company completed an expansion project that more than doubled the facility's production capabilities.

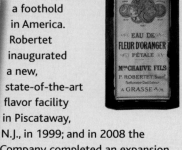

Select Products
York, Pennsylvania • Founded: 2005

From left: Umi Iswardono, president of PT Agri Spice Company; Robert Clark, CEO, CBI; and Lisa Knight, president and general manager, Select Products

Green bean picking in Java

Green bean sorting and grading in Java

Select Products is a partnership formed in 2005 between two of the largest natural vanilla bean processors and exporters in the world — Cooperative Business International (CBI) and Henri Fraise Fils & Cie — to provide vanilla and other products to North America.

Although Select Products is a recent partnership, both of its constituent companies have rich histories.

Henri Fraise started his business in Madagascar in 1918. Through various partnerships he met many customers interested in importing vanilla beans to the United States. Working through local contacts, he began to export vanilla beans from local growers, eventually involving his three sons — Rick, Georges and Ralph — in the business, which they still manage today. The Fraise operations have developed from just a few vanilla growers in the early 1900s to more than 600 farmers. The company also has diversified into a number of similar businesses such as spices.

CBI is among the world's leading international trade and market development companies, trading products such as vanilla, spices and green coffee. It was established in 1984 as a follow-on business from economic development projects funded through sources like USAID. Since then, the company has become a key supplier, responsible for 30 to 60 percent of all vanilla imported to the United States from Indonesia.

QC Lab at PT Agri Spice Company in Java

Final stage curing in Java

Organic storage and packing area in Java

Cargill Flavor Systems
Cincinnati, Ohio • Founded: 1854 (as Alex Fries & Bros.)

Flavor awards from the last half of the 20th century

After a successful career as an industrial chemist in Germany, Alexander Fries immigrated to Cincinnati, Ohio, and started a company to supply flavors to the distilling and tobacco industries in 1854. His two brothers, Harold and Gustave, joined him the next year, followed by Gustave's nephew, Dr. Alfred Springer, in the 1880s. At that time, the company was among the first to offer rum ether, gamma undecalactone (aldehyde c-140), and ethyl caproate, which are still used today to compound peach flavors.

Dr. Alfred Springer's son ran the company in the 1930s and '40s, along with a partner named Herbert Hoffheimer Jr. after World War II. In 1966, Victor Levey joined Hoffheimer, modernizing the company, building its reputation with customers and the flavor industry, and developing the first flavor to be used in isotonic drinks.

In the 1980s and '90s, the company was bought and sold to Land O'Lakes, SKW Trostberg AG, and Degussa AG. Cargill purchased Degussa's food ingredient business in 2006, combining it with its own Duckworth Flavours Ltd. to form Cargill Flavor Systems. The business unit manufactures a range of dry and liquid flavors, in addition to enzyme modified dairy flavors.

Star Kay White, Inc.

Congers, New York • Founded: 1890 (as Star Extract Works)

David Katzenstein immigrated to the United States as a boy in the early 1870s. On Valentine's Day 1890, with the support of his American-born wife, Carrie Hertz, Star Extract Works opened for business.

Within a short time they owned a factory and office in lower Manhattan, which was later the site of the World Trade Center North Tower.

Star Extract Works built its reputation on exceptional vanilla and thus became closely linked with the newly evolving ice cream industry. Chocolate, almond and peppermint extracts were early ice cream flavors.

By World War I, David Katzenstein had branched into caramel, fudge and marshmallow for ice cream under another business, Kay-White Products. Business was booming in the 1920s, so he combined both businesses into Star Kay White, Inc. and moved into new facilities in the Bronx. Then came the CRASH. Overextended, the business almost foundered.

Well, evidently we survived, and now are in transition between third, fourth and fifth generations of the Katzenstein family running Star Kay White. Still primarily focusing on ice cream flavoring ingredients, Star Kay White is proud of our roots in the flavor extract manufacturing industry. It was the quest for spices that brought Henry Hudson to American shores 400 years ago in 1609. Flavor extract manufacturers have legitimate claims to the lineage of the original Dutch colony of New Amsterdam, which is why the flavor industry was for many years located in lower Manhattan, the site of the original colony.

What a full-flavored history and heritage! We are proud to be part of it.

WORTH is a great commodity and it is the FACT that "STAR-EXTRA-GOOD XXX6XXX-VANILLA" is Worth More than it's price, because of the Fullness of Flavor It Imparts, therefore Satisfies the Natural Desire — which makes XXX6XXX-Vanilla the Favorite Winner for your business—

"See the Trade Bend to You by Bending Your Orders to Bender" COMING ABOUT

Your Business Aid

STAR EXTRACT WORKS
Office 8 W. Broadway
FACTORY
223 Greenwich St.
New York

Symrise, Inc.
Holzminden, Germany • Founded: 2003

Back in 2002, Dragoco (founded 1919) and Haarmann & Reimer (founded 1874) were two competitive companies that had much in common. Both were major flavor and fragrance suppliers based in Holzminden, Germany. Each held a legacy of success, respected for quality flavor and fragrance products, patented technologies, global R&D and manufacturing capabilities. Recognizing these complementary assets, EQT Northern Europe Private Equity acquired and merged the companies. In March 2003, Symrise was launched. Its name was selected to represent the successful symbiosis of two tradition-steeped companies. The company continues to enhance its capabilities, most recently with the acquisition of the Chr. Hansen Flavors and Seasonings business.

The tradition of quality and innovation continues at Symrise, enhanced with the energy and passion to address today's pressing industry and business issues. Dr. Matthias Guentert, President, Flavor & Nutrition Division, North America, sums it up, "As one of the leading flavor and fragrance suppliers in the United States, Symrise understands what is on the minds of customers and consumers in today's challenging economic and cultural environment. Our technological advances are complemented by our distinctive branding, structured to correspond with our customers' product positioning.

"Our view of what it takes to truly support our customers makes us true partners, building professional relationships based on knowing who we are, understanding the present and anticipating the needs of our customers, and having the insights to discern what ultimately drives consumers' needs."

Synergy Flavors, Inc.
Wauconda, Illinois • Founded: 1911

Synergy Flavors has evolved from the acquisition of various regional flavor companies by the Carbery Group, based out of Cork, Ireland. In the United States, the first acquisition was U.S. Flavors & Fragrances (based in Wauconda, Ill., and founded in 1985).

During 2004, USF&F divested its fragrance business to focus solely on flavors. The Synergy Flavors name change, completed in 2005, reflected a formal alignment with the rest of the Carbery Group's flavor businesses. The company now makes a full range of liquid and dry flavors.

Synergy remains focused on growth through acquisition, and in 2006, it acquired Vanlab (based in Rochester, N.Y., and founded in 1911), a company rich with 100 years of heritage and tradition. In early 2007 Synergy acquired AFF Aromas do Brasil to gain access to the vibrant economies of South America. In 2007, Synergy also acquired another 35,000-square-foot facility in Wauconda, Ill., to facilitate their growth.

Two global centers of excellence represent the division's headquarters. The headquarters for the Americas is located in Wauconda, Ill., and the headquarters for Europe/Asia is located in High Wycombe, England. In addition to these facilities, Synergy has additional facilities in the United Kingdom, Ireland, Thailand and Brazil that provide Synergy regionalized flavor profiles and local service on four continents.

PERCOLATORS

Specially designed percolators with accurate temperature and pressure control enables us to extract all the flavor from the Vanilla Bean.

Vanilla Laboratories, Inc. Rochester, N.Y.

All-copper percolators were replaced in the 1950s with stainless steel units.

Headquarters and manufacturing facility in Rochester, N.Y.

Sorting and bundling vanilla beans taken in Mexico

Oak holding tank and filling station for whisky barrels used for aging and shipping vanilla extract

T. Hasegawa Co. Ltd.
Tokyo, Japan • Founded: 1903

T. Hasegawa USA

For more than a century, T. Hasegawa has been a major producer of flavors and fragrances, and it is consistently rated among the Top 10 international flavor companies.

Totaro Hasegawa founded Hasegawa Totaro Shoten in1903 and began trading in flavors and fragrances. In 1941, Shozo Hasegawa succeeded his father at the company. His entrepreneurial skills and the associations he developed catapulted Hasegawa into the world flavor market. In the early days of post-World War II reconstruction, Shozo invited his college classmate, Ryoshiro Hayashi, to join the company. Together they formed T. Hasegawa Co. Ltd. in 1961 and established their headquarters in the prestigious Nihon-bashi district of Tokyo.

Shozo Hasegawa and Ryoshiro Hayashi

The two friends ambitiously grew the company into a $400 million international flavor and fragrance powerhouse. Production facilities expanded with a new plant in Fukaya in 1964, and again in Itakura in 1984. T. Hasegawa built its first overseas production facility in California in 1978, incorporated as T. Hasegawa U.S.A. Inc. The U.S. company was so successful that it built a new factory near Los Angeles in 1989 complete with extraction and reaction flavors production capacity.

In 1998, Tokujiro Hasegawa, a grandson of Totaro Hasegawa, was appointed president of the company. He has presided over Hasegawa's continuing expansion, including the opening of a full-scale flavor and fragrance factory and research facility in China. Construction on a second factory in China was scheduled to be completed in late 2009.

Totaro Hasegawa

The Coca-Cola Company
Atlanta, Georgia • Founded: 1886

Atlanta pharmacist Dr. John Stith Pemberton concocted the first Coca-Cola recipe in the 1880s and sold it for 5 cents at pharmacies as a delicious and refreshing beverage. But the soft drink really caught on when Asa Griggs Candler bought the business in 1891 and instituted the savvy marketing tactics that helped turn Coca-Cola into a consumer icon. In 1899, Benjamin F. Thomas and Joseph B. Whitehead of Chattanooga, Tenn., purchased the exclusive rights to bottle and sell Coca-Cola in most of the United States, the beginning of a large-scale soft drink bottling and distribution system that now crisscrosses the globe.

Coca-Cola's distinctive flavor has remained a consumer favorite through the decades. In fact, when the company updated its famously secret formula by introducing New Coke in 1985, public clamor for the traditional taste created a reinvigorated market for the old Coke, now dubbed Coca-Cola Classic. Since then, the company has released several new flavors, including Diet Coke sweetened with sucralose, and Coca-Cola Zero, sweetened with aspartame and acesulfame potassium.

The Hershey Company
Hershey, Pennsylvania
Founded: 1894 (as Hershey Chocolate Company)

The Hershey Company originated with candy manufacturer Milton Hershey's decision in 1894 to produce sweet chocolate as a coating for his caramels. In 1900, the company began mass-producing milk chocolate in bars, wafers and other shapes, which made milk chocolate an affordable treat. One early advertising slogan described the new product as "a palatable and a most nourishing food."

In 1907, Hershey launched its iconic HERSHEY'S KISSES, and more new products were added during the 1920s and 1930s: MR. GOODBAR, HERSHEY'S SYRUP, chocolate chips and the KRACKEL bar. With the outbreak of World War II, Hershey started producing a survival ration bar for military use. In fact, the company's machine shop even turned out parts for the Navy's antiaircraft guns.

The post-war decades saw Hershey expanding its confectionery product lines, acquiring related companies and even diversifying into other food products. Today, The Hershey Company is the largest producer of quality chocolate in North America and a global leader in chocolate and sugar confectionery.

The Procter & Gamble Company

Cincinnati, Ohio • Founded: 1837

William Procter and James Gamble might never have met if they hadn't married sisters whose father persuaded the two sons-in-law to become business partners. What began as a small, family-operated soap and candle company in Cincinnati grew and thrived, with P&G's Ivory soap representing the company's first effort at mass-marketing its products through continuous consumer advertising, starting in 1882.

P&G continued to expand in the early 20th century, building factories in other U.S. locations and diversifying into more products, including Crisco shortening. It became known for its research laboratories and pioneered market research about consumer needs and product appeal: P&G sponsored so many radio programs that the shows often became known as "soap operas."

In the second half of the 1900s, P&G diversified its product line even further and boosted profits by acquiring other companies, including Folgers Coffee, Max Factor and Iams Company. Today, Procter & Gamble is one of the world's leading consumer products companies, touching consumers' lives with brands that make life a little better every day.

Takasago International Corporation (USA)

Rockleigh, New Jersey • Founded: 1920

Takasago International Corporation was founded in Japan in 1920. For more than 80 years, Takasago has developed flavors and fragrances for some of the world's most successful food, beverage, fine fragrance, household and personal care products. Takasago is a leading global company, especially in the Asian region.

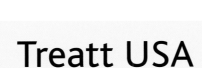

The global Takasago organization maintains offices, production sites and R&D centers in 24 countries. Through its network of global research, production, creativity and marketing, Takasago develops products tailored to the needs of individual markets.

Takasago has vigorously pursued pharmaceutical intermediaries, functional materials and other fine chemicals in which asymmetric synthesis, cultivated in its aroma chemical development work, is a key technology.

By utilizing its technologies and its global network, Takasago develops high-quality and innovative products that contribute to cultural and social progress.

Treatt USA

Lakeland, Florida • Founded: 1886

Treatt (originally pronounced "Tree-at") is one of the oldest merchant houses in the essential oil trade. Founded by Richard Court Treatt, a diplomat and former attaché in the Argentine Embassy in London, the company began trading in essential oils on London's Bond Street in 1886. Treatt gained a worldwide reputation for assessing the value of costly animal fixatives, ambergris, musk and civet, which were essential in high-class perfumes.

The business prospered, and in 1913 it was converted to a limited company. After Richard Court Treatt died in 1924, he was succeeded by A.C. Stirling. Stirling and Treatt board member E.W. Bovill, the grandfather of current managing director Hugo Bovill, expanded the company's sourcing around the world. In fact, a huge grove of bitter orange trees planted in East Africa in the early 1900s is still the source of the hand-pressed bitter orange oil Treatt buys today.

Treatt is one of the few independent citrus ingredient companies in the world, trading in more than 80 countries while sourcing essential oils, natural extracts and aromatic chemicals from more than 50 countries. In 1989 Treatt established the group's first subsidiary, Florida Treatt Inc., in Haines City, Fla., which became Treatt USA in 2002. Now based in Lakeland, Fla., Treatt USA produces natural citrus oil concentrates and specialties for juice and flavor enhancement, along with folded and terpeneless citrus oils, including the Citreatt™ and Treattarome™ F.T.N.F. range of products.

Richard Court Treatt

Vanilla Corporation of America, LLC
Hatfield, Pennsylvania • Founded: 2001

Warehouse receiving area in Sambava, Madagascar

Douglas Daugherty and his vanilla vine in Sambava, Madagascar

Founded in 2001, Vanilla Corporation of America imports, exports and distributes vanilla beans from virtually all of the vanilla-producing countries around the world. VCA is a partnership between Ykbal Hiridjee, who resides in Madagascar, and Douglas Daugherty in the United States.

Hiridjee has been involved in the vanilla trade in Madagascar since 1995. He is also the chairman and president-director general of the Trimeta Group of companies in Madagascar. Besides vanilla, the Trimeta Group is engaged as a producer and exporter of black pepper, pink pepper, cloves, cocoa and essential oils

for the food, flavor and fragrance industries. The Hiridjee family has been involved in Madagascar's commerce for many generations after first arriving in the country in 1880.

Douglas Daugherty is the second generation of the Daugherty family to be involved in the vanilla trade. Following in the footsteps of his father, who was engaged in the vanilla business for 42 years before retiring in 1993, Douglas Daugherty has more than 30 years of experience in the industry.

Vanilla bean processing center in Sambava, Madagascar

Ykbal Hiridjee and Kathy Russo inspecting some vanilla beans in the Hatfield, Penn., warehouse

Discussing new crop strategy in the Pennsylvania warehouse

Virginia Dare Extract Co., Inc.
Brooklyn, New York • Founded: 1923

With the institution of Prohibition in 1919, a North Carolina winery called Garrett & Company hired Dr. Bernard H. Smith to establish a line of flavorings that would make use of the company's alcohol. The Virginia Dare flavorings business flourished, and in 1923 Smith purchased it from Garrett and incorporated the Virginia Dare Extract Co., setting up shop in Brooklyn.

Smith was succeeded in 1952 by his son, Lloyd. Howard Smith Sr., the grandson of the founder, became president in 1960 and is currently chairman. Howard Smith Jr., the fourth generation of the family in the business, joined the company in 1984 and is currently president. All four of the Smiths served as FEMA presidents: Dr. Bernard Smith (1932-34), Lloyd Smith (1942-44), Howard Smith Sr. (1966-68) and Howard Smith Jr. (2008-09).

The headquarters, laboratories and production facilities are still located at the company's original site in Brooklyn. With proprietary extraction technology, and a thorough engagement in vanilla bean sourcing, Virginia Dare has taken a leading position in the industry and become one of the world's largest producers of vanilla extract. Its product portfolio has expanded to include tea, coffee and cocoa extracts, as well as liquid and dry flavors for a number of industries.

Whittle & Mutch, Inc.
Mt. Laurel, New Jersey • Founded: 1892

When Samuel Mutch was told by his employer, S. Twitchell Bros., that he would have little chance of advancement in a family-owned business, he decided to start his own firm. About this time his father-in-law, Samuel Whittle, had closed his millworks, leaving his son, Harry, without a job. The two young men decided to become partners, with Mutch as flavor chemist and Whittle as bookkeeper.

They rented the Nottingham Mills building on West York Street in Philadelphia, Penn., and opened Whittle & Mutch, Inc., shipping their first flavors out in August 1892. The company prospered, and Mutch later added his three sons — Sam, John and Harold — to the firm, creating his own family business. Sam, the eldest, took over the manufacturing after his father's death in 1921.

John handled sales and then supervised the laboratory until he assumed leadership of the company after Sam died. Harold ran the office and kept the books.

History repeated itself when John's two sons, John Jr. and Samuel, began running the company in 1969. Today, a fourth generation of the Mutch family — Richard and John Mutch III — is now represented on the senior management team.

Some of the company's many trademarks that are still being used include Cloud® for clouding agents and cloudy beverages such as Orange Cloud®, Lime Cloud® and Lemon Cloud®, Trucap® for dry flavors, and WAMI® (for Whittle And Mutch Inc.). Recently the company trademarked and received registration for Dixi Cola®.

Left to right: Richard L. Mutch, vice president/treasurer; John C. Mutch Jr., president; and John C. Mutch III, vice president/secretary

Wen International Inc.
Pomona, New York • Founded: 1999

The history of Wen International, which specializes in natural aroma chemicals, began with Dr. Paul Chang. In the 1970s, Dr. Chang moved his family from Taiwan to New Jersey, where the University of Delaware-educated chemist worked in the flavor and fragrance industry, including Felton International.

When mainland China opened to the Western world in the 1980s, Dr. Chang was invited to be an expert advisor by the United Nations Economic Development Council. He became the first foreign-based aroma chemist to advise China on technology development. The company was then known as Paul Trading. Natural chemical production is the result of Dr. Chang's pioneering work with the Chinese government. During the latter part of the 1980s and the 1990s, Dr. Chang was invited to lecture throughout China on flavors and fragrances, and consulted on the new business ventures of natural aroma chemicals.

Sharon Chang, his daughter and a pharmaceutical chemist, founded WEN International and continued to expand the path of novel natural materials. Today, Wen International is a major supplier of natural aroma chemicals from its longstanding collaborations with the Chinese flavor and fragrance industry.

W & g Flavors Incorporated
Hunt Valley, Maryland • Founded: 1912 (as T.H. Angermeier Company)

What would become known as W & g Flavors was founded in New York City in 1912 by Theodore Angermeier, a baker who created his own line of fillings, candy glazes, and bread and bagel bases. Products such as Black Raspberry Cool Jel, Apricot Kwik-Shine and Chocolate Kreme-Fil were all developed during the company's first few decades and are still produced and sold today.

During and after World War II, T.H. Angermeier Company was at the forefront of the revolution in dry mixes and developed the Sun-Ripe® line. With business booming in both bakery supplies and dry mixes, the company outgrew its New York City roots and moved to a larger facility in Cedar Grove, N.J., in 1959. Under the leadership of Theodore Angermeier's sons, Will and Herb, the company enjoyed great success during the 1960s and 1970s, and into the 1980s after the Angermeiers' retirement.

In 1990, a new management team headed by Wayne and Tim Wheeler assumed control of the company, and a year later it was renamed W & g Flavors and moved to Baltimore, Md. The new company expanded the product line in the foodservice segment to include dessert mixes, salad dressings, gravy mixes and artificially sweetened drink mixes for the diet market. W & g moved to a new state-of-the-art manufacturing facility in Hunt Valley, Md., in 2003.

FEMA 100th Anniversary Sponsors

Platinum

Citrus and Allied Essences Ltd. • Firmenich, Inc.

Givaudan • International Flavors & Fragrances Inc.

Kerry Ingredients & Flavours • McCormick & Company

Robertet, Inc. • Virginia Dare Extract Co., Inc.

Gold

Chuck Manley LLC • David Michael & Co., Inc. • PepsiCo

Symrise, Inc. • The Coca-Cola Company • The Roberts Group

Silver

Bell Flavors & Fragrances, Inc. • Cargill Flavor Systems

E & J Gallo Winery • Ottens Flavors • T. Hasegawa USA

Benefactor

A.M. Todd Company • Berjé, Incorporated • ConAgra Foods

Flavor & Fragrance Specialties • MANE Inc.

Nielsen-Massey Vanillas, Incorporated • Synergy Flavors, Inc.

Friend

Astral Extracts, Ltd. • Aust & Hachmann (Canada) Ltd.

Consumers Flavoring Extract Company, Inc. • Elan/Natural Flavors

Food Product Design/Virgo Publishing • Senomyx, Inc.

Sethness Products Company • Takasago International Corporation (USA)

Treatt USA • W & g Flavors Incorporated